D1632036

5/-

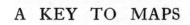

A KEY TO MAPS

PLATE I

A ROTARY OFFSET PRINTING MACHINE

Frontispiece

A KEY TO MAPS

BY

Brigadier H. S. L. WINTERBOTHAM

C.B., C.M.G., D.S.O.

Sometime Director-General of the Ordnance Survey

BLACKIE & SON LIMITED
LONDON AND GLASGOW

BLACKIE & SON LIMITED
    50 *Old Bailey, London*
    17 *Stanhope Street, Glasgow*

BLACKIE & SON (INDIA) LIMITED
    Warwick House, Fort Street, Bombay

BLACKIE & SON (CANADA) LIMITED
    Toronto

First Published May, 1936
Reprinted September, 1936

Printed in Great Britain by Blackie & Son, Ltd., Glasgow

PREFACE

To those of us who have made many maps, and
been guided by infinitely many more, it is difficult
to realize the difficulties which may beset the average
man. We turn to our maps before any and every
journey, consult them periodically, and are independent of advice and direction. Wherein lies the difficulty
for others? Principally, no doubt, in the lack of knowledge of ground itself. The map is but a conventional
portrait. Those who know, and love, the countryside
are obviously in a better position than those who do
not to form a mental picture from the map. There
are difficulties, too, of an artificial sort, introduced
into the subject for the purposes of examination. To
resect one's position on a map; to find whether A is
visible from B; above all to memorize the conventions
of this or that map; these are all affairs mainly of the
classroom. They are perfectly simple, and useful as
exercises (except for memorizing the trivial), but the
importance given to them tends to add an air of mystery
where mystery there is none. Upon a day in the War
an officer stood, map in hand, in an attitude of worry
and anger at a trench junction. To him came the
Army map man who volunteered assistance. All the
trouble was due to the fact that he had the wrong map,
which pictured quite a different part of the line.
Common sense is as useful in this as in any other
subject.

As a nation we have by far the finest map material
in the world; we have the best of all playgrounds; and

we are acquiring the map habit. It is, then, a pleasant task to endeavour to make the use of the map easier, and to add, however little, to the pleasure of our holidays, and to the knowledge of our countryside.

The history of mapping is a fascinating study, but one not necessary to the understanding of modern maps. It is not dealt with here except in so far as it affects the maps we may still use. As far as possible the practical points of map use have been dealt with, and everything else avoided. Chapter IV on map projections is perhaps an exception. It is, however, perfectly possible to get a general idea of the subject in the comfort of an easy chair, and without touching upon the mathematical side. Chapters on Geological Maps, and upon the Weather Map, have been added in answer to special requests. The book ends with a brief description of the process of map-making in the field and office. The chapter on the Fieldwork of Mapping is taken, practically unaltered, from *The Listener*, in which it appeared as a record of a broadcast talk.

Throughout, plans and maps are referred to by the names commonly used for them, without a full description of scale or representative fraction.

Thus:

The *Ten-foot*, and *Five-foot* Plans are those at ten and five feet to the mile respectively. Representative fractions 1/528 (or 1/500) and 1/1056, respectively.

The *Twenty-five inch* is the ordinary plan at 1/2500.

The *Six-inch* is the six inch to one mile (1/10,560).

The *One-inch* is the one inch to one mile (1/63,360).

The *Half-inch* is the half-inch to one mile (1/126,720).

The *Quarter-inch* is the quarter-inch to one mile (1/253,440).

The *Ten-mile* is the ten mile to one inch (1/633,600).

The 1/M is the 1/1,000,000, or 15·78 miles to one inch.

The 1/2M is the 1/2,000,000, or 31·56 miles to one inch.

The 1/4M is the 1/4,000,000, or 63 miles to one inch.

Most books on maps include examples printed in full colour. This book does not, for two good reasons. In the first place the size of page is too small to do them justice, and in the second no one else can produce such excellent samples, and so cheaply, as the Ordnance Survey. The *Description of the Ordnance Survey Small Scale Maps*, eighth edition, 1s., includes twenty colour plates, amongst which appear all the ordnance maps mentioned in this book.

Perhaps a word of apology is due to the preoccupation of this book with Ordnance Survey publications and processes. Many other good maps are made. But it is easiest for the cobbler to stick to his last.

I desire to express my gratitude to the Director General of the Ordnance Survey, Brigadier M. N. MacLeod, D.S.O., M.C., for his kindly assistance, and for permission to include certain plates and figures; to Rear-Admiral J. A. Edgell, O.B.E., R.N., the Hydrographer, to Sir George Simpson, K.C.B., C.B.E., F.R.S., of the Meteorological Office, and to Doctor Bernard Smith, M.A., F.R.S., of the Geological Survey and Museum, for their help, and for allowing an amateur to skirmish within their borders; to Sir Stenson Cooke, for a helpfulness as characteristic of himself as of the Automobile Association; to Mr. A. O'Dell for much valuable advice, and, most of all, to many old friends and comrades of the Ordnance Survey who have assisted with enthusiasm.

CONTENTS

LIST OF PLATES

A KEY TO MAPS

CHAPTER I

Map, Plan, and Chart

MOST of us, except in our more poetical moments, are clear as to the difference between a map and a chart. We do not normally talk of uncharted forests or unmapped seas. For all that there is a distinct overlap between the words. The craftsmanship of map-making is called cartography and the French " carte " and German " karte " (meaning map in both cases) tend to confuse the chart and the map. Both map and chart, of course, are principally concerned with solid earth, but the map deals with the uncovered, and the chart with the submerged, portion. The one records everything above a water surface, the other everything below. There remains a neutral ground. The chart must and does show the coasts in sufficient detail to make clear the lie and position of all aids to coastal navigation. Often we have been, and sometimes we still are, indebted to the hydrographer for the only reliable presentation of land surface. There are still, for example, some of the West Indian islands " unmapped ", except for the " chart "; and on most maps which include parts of the coast you will find submarine contours, taken from chart material, to give a rough idea of the dangers

1

and possibilities of approach. A famous British Hydro-grapher—Captain W. H. Smyth—who charted the coasts of Italy early in last century was one of the first to show how important and satisfactory a com-bination of land and sea surveying can be. He worked in close conjunction with Austrian and Neapolitan officers of the land survey. Gradually this principle is spreading and, whilst the land surveyor and hydro-grapher have their distinct and separate spheres, their maps and charts borrow increasingly from each other for the convenience of the public.

The border line between a plan and a map is more difficult to draw. Indeed, to many of us, the word map reigns supreme in cartography, whilst a " plan " suggests some deep-laid scheme for the pacification of Europe or the defeat of an enemy. Nevertheless both words are officially in use for the mapping of Great Britain, and are common in the literature con-nected with it. No doubt the word " plan " was origin-ally used more in connexion with property surveys, in the same sort of way as an architect or builder will talk of his plans. The sheets of that wonderful national achievement, the published survey at 1/2500, are known as the " twenty-five-inch plans ", and the still more widely used six-inch as the " six-inch plans ". If you ask a map agent for a twenty-five-inch or six-inch map you will certainly get it, but there may be a smile on the face of the agent. Normally the line between maps and plans (the small scales and the large) is drawn just below the six-inch, everything smaller in scale being known as a map.

There may be many who have never possessed a plan and who do not realize how much those large scales enter into, and influence, every-day life. The census would be hardly possible without them; the transfer of property even more cumbrous than to-day. We are, almost without exception, interested in rights of way, either as landowners or as seekers after fresh air and exercise. But these are best seen on the six-inch plans, and are now being officially investigated on them. The innumerable authorities, who look after our affairs, supply us with some things and tax us for all, plan their works and incidences on the twenty-five or the six-inch. Road developments, changes of boundaries, title redemptions, mining activities, investigations of title, all these and many other essential matters demand accurate plans. Even where one can, at a pinch, do without plans, how much easier they may make life. Think, for example, of that plan of the vegetable garden which takes perhaps a couple of hours of a winter evening to make, and which shows the gardener exactly where to plant without transgressing the proper rotation. There are the old ones of the last few years just to show what to avoid. How else shall a jobbing gardener be kept clear in his mind or avoid inserting a furtive row of cabbages on last year's brussel sprout bed? Of our own city or town a " town plan " is the greatest assistance both to ourselves and to our visitors, especially if it has with it a good gazetteer of street names and a good way of describing where, upon the plan, to find the street in question. Town plans of this sort are, however, generally rather sketchy affairs. Their purpose is that of the railway map in Bradshaw. They show relative position, go in for no elaboration, and, generally, are on poor paper. Their virtue is to direct the curious, and to cost little. Many desire more information about their immediate surroundings than such plans normally give. For example, it is pleasant to know exactly how much ground goes with " this desirable residence ", and how neighbouring houses and properties lie. The plan which goes with the title deeds is generally, though not always, derived from an ordnance plan, omits many details and confines itself entirely to the one property. The ordnance plan gives all the details, and, if the property lies outside a built-up area, gives the exact acreage. The ordnance plan will show you the boundaries within which the various local authorities collect their dues; whether if you buy such and such a house there is room for a tennis court; what paths in the neighbourhood are available for exercising the dog; and will satisfy a quite legitimate curiosity as to the neighbours. There is a question, of course, as to drainage. The 6-inch plan gives all the contours and bench-marks.

The land agent, the official, and the numerous unpaid who help in the administration of country life, must, of course, have these plans. The preservation of places of national interest, town and district planning, road schemes, and the like cannot be conducted without. As citizens, we need not be dependent upon these gentlemen for our knowledge of our own particular surroundings. We can take the shortest cuts, quote the correct local names, identify the local antiquities, and follow, with intelligence, the progress of the electric grid and the new water supply by a glance at the appropriate plan.

Here comes in the question of scale. At one time the national series of plans included the 10- and 5-foot plans. With the larger of these two scales (the 10-foot) it is easy enough (with a well-divided scale or ruler) to measure lengths on the plan correct to a foot, and, of course, one must double this " uncertainty " for the 5-foot plans. Alas these most useful plans have been allowed to fall into decay, but it is probable that any town house or property built before 1885 or so will be found upon them. Curiously enough London was never surveyed at the larger scale, but it is probable that the 5-foot plans of London will be revised. In towns then a 10-foot or 5-foot plan with the corresponding 6-inch plan will be the ideal combination, and if it be London, and the subsoil is a matter of interest, a geological 6-inch can be got from the Geological Museum. If the house is new and the neighbourhood is changed much

a 25-inch plan and its corresponding 6-inch must
serve, and these two are of even greater help in the
village. Next, of course, a real tragedy may happen.
You are, you find, exactly in the corner of both the
25-inch and 6-inch. This is a situation which repeats
itself unceasingly in peace and war. There is nothing
to be done but to acquire all four! A few details as to
mounting them together are given later on.

The 6-inch is the smallest plan, and the 1-inch the
largest map. That leaves an unpleasantly large gap
which is filled almost everywhere else in Europe by
maps of $2\frac{1}{2}$ or 3 inches to the mile (roughly). A map
at this sort of scale is often very useful. It will show
footpaths and field divisions if the latter are largish.
Things do not have to be much exaggerated in size,
as they do on the 1-inch in order to appear plainly.
The lack of this medium scale in England is explained
by the publication of the 25-inch and 6-inch. The
one and only original survey of Great Britain is made
for the 25-inch, whereas abroad the original survey is
only at some such scale as 6 inches to the mile and is
published at half the scale of survey. We suffer in
this minor particular because we are by far the best
mapped country of the world. The camera can be
called in, however, and there are many who have
procured photographic reductions, from the 6-inch, to
such scales as 2 or 3 inches to the mile. Some of the
outlying islands have good maps already on these
medium scales. Guernsey has a 3-inch, Jersey and the
Scilly Islands 2-inch maps, and so has Malta. Hong
Kong has a 1/20,000 (nearly 3-inch), and Johore a
1/25,000 (or $2\frac{1}{2}$-inch).

There may be many who have never possessed either
a plan or a chart, but there must be few who have
never used a map. They range from an inch to a mile,
to hundreds of miles to the inch, and those who love
to divide up everything into pigeon holes divide them,
as they get smaller in scale, into topographical, geo-

graphical and atlas. The last, described by a very intelligent schoolgirl as the earth put through a mangle, are not touched upon in this book; and the first two, both of them really topographical *and* geographical, range from 1-inch to the mile to about 30 miles to the inch.

Quite apart from the fact that maps are the indispensable stocktaking upon which public affairs are conducted, and defence measures planned, they are of the greatest assistance to our holiday travels. Map sales continue to increase, whether money is cheap or dear. They are at once the guide to our pleasantest ramblings and a record of them. No one can avoid factories and cobbled streets, and pick a skilful path through unspoiled country, without them. No one can get the best from his holiday neighbourhood without his 1-inch. But there is no one particular sort of map to serve all purposes, and in this matter we in Great Britain have a quite peculiar wealth of choice. When a country first begins to make reliable maps it is natural that it should concentrate on one particular scale (say 1-inch to the mile) and should proceed to build up, one after the other, a regular series of sheets of fixed dimensions. If the purchaser of one is in a corner there he must stay. At that stage there will be no particular sheets for holiday areas, nor any "derived scales ", or reductions (say ½-inch or ¼-inch) to deal more adequately with fast modern travel. The 1-inch of Great Britain was such a survey during most of last century. It was, however, wisely designed to fill the wants of administrator, soldier, and civilian alike, and as perhaps the hunting community would cover more ground than others the map was often known as " the Hunting Map ". There are lots of things to say about this 1-inch, and they will be dealt with later on. It will be sufficient to emphasize here that no smaller scale can fulfil the same functions or include boundaries, rough classification of forests, symbols for parks, and national reserves, roads as low down in category as bridle paths, antiquities and golf courses, inns and telephone call-boxes, or, what is perhaps more valuable still, 50-foot contours. If areas, and points about property, are not actually in question, the 1-inch is a nearly perfect guide to the country round.

There are, however, many occasions when something of wider area (and therefore of smaller scale) is required. The mountains of Scotland and Wales are mostly crowned with cairns which record the progress of the great trigonometrical survey of 1830 or so. Supposing we stand by one of them and look around. What is that imposing peak some 15 or 20 miles away? Probably it will not be on the 1-inch sheet at all, but far beyond its limited range. The $\frac{1}{2}$-inch or $\frac{1}{4}$-inch must be brought into play. Or again motoring to one's holiday haunts there will first arise the question of the best road to pursue. Our most helpful motoring associations will give us admirable routes and full details, but we may wish to visit this friend, or that particular town, and the emergency may develop at the last moment. A 1-inch is too big in scale. We should have to carry too many of them, and again, the $\frac{1}{2}$-inch, $\frac{1}{4}$-inch or 10-mile will provide the easiest answer.

In many countries overseas there is far less to show on a map than in the thickly populated and thoroughly developed English countryside. In Kenya, or Southern Rhodesia, or Natal, for example, a $\frac{1}{4}$-inch will show all that the traveller needs. So large, relatively, are the properties in South Africa that a $\frac{1}{2}$-inch will show farm boundaries in much the same way as the 6-inch of England. In such places the smaller scales take the place, at present anyhow, of the 1-inch, and still smaller scales are required for the "general idea". It is recorded of a very intrepid and famous air-woman that she landed "somewhere in Africa" asking, "Am I in Kenya, Uganda or Tanganyika". Under circumstances so intriguing as these a map at the very small scale of 1 in 2 million (roughly 32 miles to the inch) seems indicated, and having travelled over most of Africa in a car I can vouch for the fact that the admirable War Office series at that scale serves much the same purpose as the $\frac{1}{4}$-inch at home. There is, one perceives, no hard and fast law as to scales. Every man must suit his own purpose and study the indexes to the maps of official or private map-makers to see what they have to offer. The outstanding fact is that every man who wishes to take advantage of a fine day, who is content to guide himself and not content to follow implicitly the directions of others, must have a detailed map of his immediate surroundings and a much smaller scale one, upon which the wings of fancy and the wheels of his car may find room to roam.

How many happy memories many of us have of holidays on the water. Strong tea, eggs and bacon on a tin plate, jerseys and gum-boots, that night we dragged anchor, and the afternoon we very nearly spent on the Spitway. Sunny or stormy days alike, however, the most useful thing aboard is the chart case. There are no difficulties of consequence in chart reading and it is well that it is so, for otherwise how many more low tides would we all spend at a very uncomfortable angle. In sea travel, as in land, there are two demands to be made on the chart or map. The general idea, the scheme of the cruise, the best course for the occasion, demand a small scale, while the particulars and points of harbour or creek demand a large. Charts are not produced in the same sort of universal series as maps. Scales are just what are required to show the objects in view. Thus a large scale chart will take in not only the harbour or river reach in question, but such navigation marks, whether natural or artificial, as are required for that area. There is a chart of the British Isles at 25 sea miles to the inch and others of Cowes Harbour and Lower

Loch Tarbert at 29 inches and 15 inches to the sea mile respectively. More will be said presently on this matter of chart scales, because, from the projection on which they are plotted (the Mercator), the scale can never be constant (but only reasonably so) over any one sheet. In navigation, however, distances are not the main factor, but directions. To get things in line and so find position is the essence of the game, and every map user has much to learn from this fact. It is curious to note that the hydrographer divides his material into oceanic, general, coastal, and approach charts and ends off, just as does the land surveyor, in large-scale " plans ". If you ever want to " survey the world around " pick up a catalogue of Admiralty charts and visit in fancy such places as " Pango Pango Harbour " and " Thimble Tickles ".

It has been said that just as the landsman and the sailor have mapped and charted their respective elements so must the airman map his. There is here a fundamental misconception. The sailor does not map his element, but all the perils of solid earth which beset travel upon it. So it must be for airmen. There are many sorts of maps for airmen now, but the best possible answer has not yet been found, nor will be until, from the air, all those objects—roads, railways, lakes, buildings, or even golf courses—have been identified which are easily visible as well from the air as on the map and useful therefore as navigation marks. The only thing which, logically, can be called an air map is a meteorological chart (the weather map) and of that we shall talk later.

As a last general word never expect plan or map to be exactly up to date. Maps must be made and do not fall like manna from heaven. They do not generally appear on the bookstalls until the surveyors have left the ground for some months. They are not revised every day, and meanwhile houses spring up by the thousand, forestry officials are busy, reservoirs and electric grids appear, and, perhaps, votes are cut and revision postponed. Abroad, if development is less hasty than with us, maps are generally much further in arrear. There is perhaps nothing in life so tiresome as the perfect article against which we can find no reproach. The occasional lapse you may discover in the maps you buy will but witness to your own observant nature.

CHAPTER II

The Night Before

HAD Sir Walter Scott looked at Roy's Map of the Highlands the night before beginning to write *Waverley*, and chosen certain extracts therefrom, he would have saved himself and his readers a weary hour or two. Had the British Army secured a good map of the locality, and studied it the night before, a famous Horse Artillery Battery would not have had occasion to win so many Victoria Crosses at Sannah's Post. Had diplomats always made a habit of studying the map the night before agreeing upon international boundaries, confusion would have been avoided.

In the ordinary affairs of the average person many minor tragedies occur for the same reason. No doubt these are mainly in connexion with travel, but having had to do with many changes of locality and the search for many new houses I want to start with that problem. Perhaps the locality is fixed within broad limits or perhaps one starts with all Great Britain to pick and choose from. In any case innumerable notices, pink, blue, and yellow, dealing with this or that " desirable modern residence " descend upon one. These are amplified by the cuttings from advertisement columns, sent by kind and helpful friends. The name of the residence in question is qualified by its distance from a railway station. No map is ever supplied. When, after much trouble, the place is found, a glance may show that the country, the aspect, or the approaches, make it unuitable for your purpose. The house may lie too low or too high, or it may have no view. It may be too near to, or too far from, a main road. These are all facts which the map would have shown " the night before ". Then again it is a difficult question to arrange the order and time of visit. Two friends of mine discussed the problem the other day in this fashion. " How did you find that charming little house?" she said. " Well," he replied, " it was the 71st we saw." " You are lucky," was the answer, " we are living in the 327th." Having fixed a locality to search in, tabulate all the alternatives in the margin of the map. Place them on the ground, and see whether the map itself will not eliminate a considerable percentage. Number the remainder in order of travel, and note where a good view over the whole area is likely.

A similar problem is that of the parents who want to take the family to a quiet beach, somewhere far from charabancs, where the sand is clean and solitude spells peace. Here again is occasion to tabulate alternatives on a map and to eliminate the obviously un-desirable. The best holiday of my recollection, with a cove practically inaccessible except from a tiny village, was due entirely to the map.

The modern rambler is, generally, an expert map reader. Like others who use their maps frequently, he studies his travels more thoroughly the night before than when he is on the road. England is so crowded to-day that we cannot take the risk of going the wrong way and coming back to just that type of town or country which we wish to avoid. Nor does the previous appeal to the map spoil the adventure. To choose one's own way and walk at no man's dictation is still the aim. As regards maps there is practically no choice. The 1-inch is the obvious solution, at any rate as the companion for the day's tramp. Some thought, however, should go to the selection of the sheets. There are many tourist and district sheets such as those of Loch Lomond, the Lake District, the Peak District,

Ilkley Moor, Snowdon, the Middle Thames, the New Forest, the Norfolk Broads, and so on. Altogether there are 58 of these special maps, any one of which may save the purchase of two or three ordinary sheets. There are some cases, however, in which a ½-inch may prove as useful. For example, in the Highlands and in Wales, there is less for the map to show, and at the same time views are longer. It is a comfort to be able to place what one can see. An admirable ½-inch of the Island of Skye serves most purposes there except perhaps for an intensive campaign in the Cuillins. The rambler's " night before " can be left to the 1-inch or ½-inch he is to carry. It is fairly good going to walk over a 1-inch sheet in a day.

The ½-inch is as natural to the cyclist as the 1-inch to the rambler. Footpaths are not of the same importance, though inns may be. There is enough detail, at any rate, for country which is to be passed through rather than explored. Here again there are special or district sheets such as those of the London Traffic Area, the Cotswolds, and Birmingham. At the same time, if a cycle tour is to consist of a ride to holiday quarters and a stay there of some days, it would often be best to use the ¼-inch for the night before and the journey to and fro, and to carry the 1-inch sheet which covers the holiday area.

Directly the holiday adventure takes to wheels the importance of the night before rises with a bound. It becomes a question of finding one's way at anything from 10 to 60 miles an hour, and most of us want to see and enjoy the country. We do not want to wrestle with a map, or to condemn our wives to do it for us. Of course it is sometimes necessary, but nothing like so often as many think. Many, in their several ways of getting over the land, belong to federations or associations. These will issue routes accompanied by occasional plans and sketches. All these want to be followed out on a map, however. The route speaks of such and such a turning as (say) $3\frac{1}{4}$ miles from Broughby. But none of us have so accurate a measure of distance as will stop us infallibly at the right point. If the distance is put into time the same difficulty crops up. We may be deterred by the grim lady in the Baby Austin holding the right edge of the crown of the road. There may be road repairs and the watchman, having his lunch, may be satisfied to turn "Go" to "Stop" for a period too long for our comfort. The answer is to go over the road on the map the night before and make certain that the right corner is obvious when we get there. It is not enough to count turnings and to think (say) of the fifth to the left after passing the White Hart. There are often turnings into some blind alley or private property not apparent on the map, but evident on the ground, and the builder may have been busy with new development roads. When we have once been over a road we remember that the turning in question was just before a church with a spire, or just after passing under a railway bridge, or over the stream which had followed the north side of the road for a mile or two, or perhaps just after passing the cricketers' P.H. But all these things are also on the map. It is the mental picture which is at fault if the map has not helped. Often enough the most conspicuous feature in the vicinity will be a hill, a mound, or a gradient. To visualize these from the map is easy enough if one takes the trouble to look at contours as well as detail. The link between map and country lies in those features which you are bound to see and notice as you approach them. Look for those very things on the map the night before. Perhaps the most obvious features of all are bridges. We go over them and under them, leave them on our right or left, and see them carrying trains or lorries. The power lines of the electric grid are not on all the maps yet, but are also conspicuous affairs.

A difficulty of forging a link between map and

country is that the slightest bend of a road on the map may turn into a very noticeable corner on the ground. Looking ahead from some five or six feet above ground level emphasizes the importance of the sideways and foreshortens the view. Moreover the map has, for lack of space, to generalize a bit. Indeed, on the map a road may seem quite straight where it bends sufficiently to shut out all forward view.

With the above points in mind, ten minutes on the map the night before, and an occasional glance at the signposts, the way should be easily found. There are, however, one or two other points to note. On foot, on a bicycle, or in a car an occasional halt is desirable, and meals may be in question. If possible these occasions (at any rate on a holiday) deserve some forethought. If it is just a halt, why not look along the route and see where you can sit at ease and look over the countryside at the same time. Have you never stopped on the scarps of Chilterns, Cotswolds or Mendips; never looked over the weald of Kent from Bluebell Hill, or seen the Wallop Brook and its valley opening out as you top the hill from Romsey? If not, it is certainly time you did. Great Britain abounds in these sudden panoramas, not so extensive perhaps as that over the Rift Valley in Kenya, in the Rockies or in Cashmere, yet with an intimate charm which is unique. Why not look for the opportunity the night before and not pass it at forty miles an hour? Perhaps, however, you prefer to follow the directions on those route maps which exhort you to stop and look in the direction of the purple arrow for the view. Then consider the matter of lunch or tea (or best of all breakfast on a summer morning). It is a matter of astonishment how many family parties may be seen on the dusty margin of a Class A road eating sandwiches to the accompaniment of hoots and exhausts. Whiffs of petrol, thin mists of dust, seem to leave them unperturbed. Yet down on the left at the next turning one comes to a meadow by a stream, or up on the right to the downs. There is probably not ten minutes' delay in it. All such occasions cannot be foreseen but a great many can. "That would be a grand spot for lunch if we are thereabouts at one o'clock."

Owner-drivers do well to belong to one or the other of our most helpful motoring associations. Not only do they assist in many other ways, but their routes and signs, loopways and scouts, are an ever-present help in finding where to go. There are many who make a sudden dash to the holiday centre. From London to Inverness, from Southampton to Land's End, or from Bristol to the Norfolk Broads. For such trips the shortest route is the thing. The moors call, the boat is at her moorings, or Jones expects his revenge on the links to-morrow. Even those who have more time will want a route through unpopular districts or a really up-to-date traffic plan of some town, or information about the roads in an unfamiliar place. In all such cases prepared routes and up-to-date town diagrams are advisable, but the map is wanted as well.

The night before may well develop into the week before for the owner-driver, and first of all he wants a map to cover the whole area of his travels. It is only on such a map that one can plan properly. Great Britain is not very large, but at the same time it is rather big to get on a single sheet considering the information one wants. There are maps at the scale of one in a million which cover the whole and show the roads with a few details added. These are not good enough for the purpose. It is a great mistake to think that a map of the roads is enough. The smallest scale map which gives a good idea of the rise and fall, enough names, and enough small roads is the 10-mile.

A 10-mile (fully coloured), Ansell folded (see Chapter XII), will cover Great Britain. It is good enough to plan on, and good enough to answer innumerable questions by the way. Such questions as " Where should we be now if we had chosen the western route?" " Are we as far south as Oxford?" " Is it too late to cut across to see such and such a place?" cannot well be answered without a good and inclusive map, and, moreover, one which can be used as a whole and is not cut into innumerable snippets. Ten miles to one inch is not far from twice as big as the one in a million, but is the smallest scale which really helps the curious. It is certainly the map for " the week before " and should find a place in the map pocket of the car.

The 10-mile is hardly the map for the " night before ", however; especially in new country. The ¼-inch is the ideal scale for that purpose. Let me quote an illustrative case. There is a charming moorland road from Barnards Castle to Alston. On a certain June evening an owner-driver, heading that way, stayed at a famous hostelry on the Great North Road. He dined next to two adventurous damsels. One had, before her, a black-and-white road diagram cut from the pages of an enterprising daily. It showed a network of roads, a name or two, and an imposing title. It gave no hint of stream or gradient, of moor or forest. It looked a sorry thing to base a holiday upon. The other evidently felt as much for she said: " I believe that road is rather hilly; I wish the map gave gradients." " Jane, how can you be so silly?" answered the first. " If Keren-happuch could hear you she would boil with indignation." Keren-happuch (one wonders what her horn really *was* made of) was an early starter, and so it was that the next meeting found her near the top of one of the gradients. She *was* boiling, and far below the two damsels could be seen filling a kettle, and what looked like a hat, at the stream.

The ¼-inch gives every road that one may go on, and a surprising amount of general information. The hill features are good and contours (at a vertical interval of 200 feet) are twice as numerous as on the 10-mile. There is enough on it to give a real picture of the ground and to make it easy to memorize a route " the night before ".

Then there is one further question to consider. A motorist trapped in the intricacies of an unfamiliar town is a nuisance to himself and to everyone else. But these intricacies need not be so dreadful. Let us take the case of a wanderer, who, after touring the Highlands, and spending two or three days sight-seeing in Edinburgh, is due to start off, bright and early, next morning for the south. He has already, mark you, picked up his " general map " (the 10-mile, let us say) and decided whether he shall go by the east, the middle, or the west (they are all delightful). Then he will wonder how to find his way through these solid, well-planned squares, gardens, and terraces, to the road of his choice. Is it to be left to his wife and the policeman on traffic duty, or can the problem be solved in advance? It can. Within the covers of the $\frac{1}{4}$-inch he will find a traffic diagram. Now it is only the motor associations who keep sufficiently up-to-date to record all the most recent developments. It might be that our friend was furnished with one of their town plans. But if not; if the visit to Edinburgh was unpremedi-tated, the diagram in the $\frac{1}{4}$-inch is amply good enough. If repairs are in the way A.A. loopway signs will signal the fact. This again is a case for the night before.

What is then the map armoury for a motorist?

A general map covering the whole area.

A set of $\frac{1}{4}$-inch maps (or, if these are not carried, a book of town diagrams).

A 1-inch of any place where a few days' halt may be made.

An A.A. handbook.

It is a matter of opinion what form the $\frac{1}{4}$-inch maps should take. Some (and I confess to being amongst them) like to carry Ansell folded copies. Four cover Great Britain. Scotland falls wholly upon one. Because, so mounted, these contain no traffic diagrams, I carry a book of collected diagrams, and one such is sold by the Ordnance Survey.

Maps are seldom required more, or consulted less, than on sea voyages which include days here and there in harbour. Maps never seem to be available on the boat itself and one is left to wrestle with an unfamiliar language or to patronize a guide. Now a human guide may be a help, but is often a bore, and the string of earnest faces in his wake induces a feeling of solemnity not always seasonable. If proper maps are available, and they can easily be made so, then the night before port is as important as the night before starting off in the car. The sights may be listed from guide books (which the ship can generally produce), identified on the map and enjoyed in peace. We need not linger too long over St. Sebastian, nor jostle that earnest spinster who is anxious not to miss a single word.

Ships bring up the question of charts. Is there anything pleasanter than to end up an eventful day on one's own boat by studying the next day's run on the chart, and speculating on whether the weather forecast (if correct!) will allow us to make such and such a harbour? It is, however, as much urgent business as pleasure. He is a wise yachtsman who plans ahead with a few alternatives up his sleeve. I assume, of course, that he has the necessary charts with him, both large and small.

CHAPTER III

Map Conventions

AS the first thing to do is to get out the right map it will be well to start this chapter with a word on the Title and the Number. Both are given on the map itself and on the cover, and both should be remembered. The title is the name of some one or two cities or towns. The title alone, supposing that it consists of one town name, may suggest that that town is right in the middle of the sheet. Such an impression would be often misleading, and there is no excuse for being misled, for on the cover a little diagram shows the area covered, and the places of importance which fall within it. Turn the cover over and see if there is an index to sheets on the back. If there is, it will show you how the sheet numbers run, and what others you may need. The fifth edition of the ordnance 1-inch has an excellent habit of adding, just inside the covers, diagrams showing how half and quarter-inch sheets cover the same area.

Now to think of the scale. We have all been photographed so often that there is no excuse for being shaky on scales. If all these photographs had been life-size how bulky the family album would be. Here, for example, is a baby, a little doubled up, and taking $2\frac{1}{2}$ inches of the photograph. At that tender age the baby's height (minus the doubling) was about two feet. The scale then is $2\frac{1}{2}$ inches to 2 feet, or $\frac{2\cdot5}{24}$, which gives the "Representative Fraction", as it is called, of about $\frac{1}{10}$. Here is a snapshot of the same baby grown to a six-footer. He takes 1 inch of photograph, so now the scale is 1 inch to 6 feet, or $\frac{1}{72}$. Owing to our odd, but very human, units of measurement, we think seldom in " Representative Fractions ". " Half inch to the mile " is, for example, much more enlightening than 1/126,720. The inches are easily estimated by eye and the number of miles on the ground, represented by those inches, we can visualize well enough. For the every-day use of maps no more precise measure of distance is required, since we cannot journey as the crow flies.

It may, however, be convenient to remember that the diameter of a halfpenny is exactly an inch, an ordinary safety match is about two inches, and the hand, pressed down upon the map palm downwards and thumb extended to its full extent, will not be far from six inches from edge of palm to tip of thumb. Plan scales are usually known, in the same fashion, as so many feet or inches to the mile. There are some tiresome people who give us no direct clue except for a scale drawn or printed at the bottom of the map or plan labelled " scale of miles ", or " scale of feet ". That is taking an unfair advantage because it gives no mental picture. A scale labelled " 10 chains to the foot " is a similar nuisance to most of us if no representative fraction is added, because few could visualize a chain length or even remember that it is sixty-six feet. Representative fractions become immediately necessary in using foreign maps. The idea of so many centimetres to the kilometre will also fail to give most Englishmen a mental picture.

It is easy to establish the fact that 1·6093 kilometres go to the mile, but it is quite a different thing to reckon familiarly in them. We know that about $2\frac{1}{2}$ centimetres go to the inch but the eye is unaccustomed to measure in terms of them. Before decimal scales can be adopted with real profit we must learn to think decimally. In 1808 Napoleon was in exactly this same position. He had urgent need of maps of Germany at that time.

The military mapping authorities in Paris suggested a scale of 1/100,000. Napoleon replied, "I am not at all in agreement with your proposals, and scoff at your decimal scales." He and his generals thought in leagues and toises, and for them these were the essential factors of a scale. As a French friend described it: "A l'égard du système métrique, l'Empereur était en quelque sorte comme . . . un Anglais." It must not be thought, however, that we are quite without decimal units. The Gunter's chain (of 100 links or 66 feet) was invented to decimalize measurement of acres. For the larger distances of small scale maps we still think instinctively in miles and inches, but for many years all ordnance maps have borne a scale of kilometres as well as one of yards, so that the decimally minded, and our foreign guests, may also feel at home.

The first thing to do then with metrical maps is to work out how many inches represent a mile or how many miles go to the inch at that scale. Supposing that the representative fraction of a map is $\frac{1}{300,000}$, and knowing that the representative fraction of the 1-inch is $\frac{1}{63,360}$, a proportional sum does the rest. The answer is that $\frac{300,000}{63,360}$ or 4·75 miles (roughly) go to the inch.

It may be as well to tabulate some of the more ordinary foreign scales:

$\frac{1}{10,000}$	is nearly	6 inches to the mile.
$\frac{1}{20,000}$	,,	3 inches to the mile.
$\frac{1}{25,000}$	,,	$2\frac{1}{2}$ inches to the mile.
$\frac{1}{50,000}$	,,	$1\frac{1}{4}$ inches to the mile.
$\frac{1}{80,000}$	,,	$\frac{3}{4}$ inch to the mile.
$\frac{1}{100,000}$	,,	A little more than $\frac{6}{10}$ inch to the mile. May be taken very very roughly to correspond to the $\frac{1}{2}$ inch.
$\frac{1}{200,000}$	,,	3 miles to the inch.
$\frac{1}{250,000}$	,,	4 miles to the inch (the quarter inch).
$\frac{1}{300,000}$	,,	5 ($4\frac{3}{4}$) miles to the inch.
$\frac{1}{500,000}$	,,	8 miles to the inch.

Converting to our own ideas in this way means, however, that one must convert the kilometres of signposts and guide-books into the miles of one's mind and speedometer.   A kilometer is 0·62 of a mile.   It is near enough to take $\frac{3}{5}$ths[1] ($\frac{6}{10}$ths will be more convenient) of the number of kilometres as representing the corresponding number of miles.   Before leaving the question of scales there is room for serious warning. Convenience often dictates the size of the map. A famous old English map-maker once confessed that had there been more room on his parchment the scale might have been larger.   The fact minus the apology may be found to occur in quite well-known atlases which give, below the maps, representative fractions not always so really descriptive as they might be. But besides errors of convenience there are shrinkages or expansions of the paper itself to consider.   Paper swells when wet, contracts when dry, and errors of a hundredth part of any length may often be due to this fact. The holiday-maker will not be troubled, but the geographical student will. Let him, or her, measure up carefully before basing fresh work upon an existing map, and remember too that paper expansions differ according to the direction of the grain (or way in which the paper was rolled). The extent of distortion, or unequal expansion, may be of the order of one part in three hundred.

The next point of importance is the North Point. It is curious, when one thinks of it, that all modern maps put the north on top.   It is as true of South Africa as of Great Britain.   Yet it used not to be so. Map-makers of the Middle Ages would suit their orientation to their paper. Nowadays we need have no fear on that score, but we must be careful to remember that orientation to the north is not exact in all cases. It is often assumed that the eastern and western edges of ordnance survey maps point true north and

---

[1] $\frac{3}{5}$ths is more accurate than $\frac{2}{3}$ths, but is not quite so easy to establish.

south. That is not the case. British maps, official and private, are generally rectangular, and with very good reason, because they join up so very much better when they are. Any map which insisted on being rectangular in shape and yet being bounded by lines truly north and south would make the scale at Aberdeen substantially larger than at London. Now charts do this, but for a very good reason which will appear in the chapter on projections. Maps do not, and as we get to the eastern and western coasts of Great Britain, say East Anglia and Skye respectively, the margins begin to draw perceptibly away from true north and south. The north point, which is almost always in the right-hand, or eastern margin, has, therefore, three lines to it. True north, magnetic north and sheet line (or grid) north. These refer to the centre of the map. Two or three degrees, one way or another, are of no moment to the ordinary map user, but they may make a difference in special cases. This matter will be dealt with at greater length therefore in Chapter X.

Conventional signs deserve little consideration here because they introduce so little difficulty and confuse so few people. In fact, for the traveller, it is best to keep an open mind. Very few maps are published without a list, and illustrations, of the conventional signs used upon them. These are always given in the southern margin.

Many signs show the objects they represent in elevation instead of in plan. This idea has one drawback. It is not easy to say, in such a case, where the object should be in plan. Lighthouses and windmills are cases in point. On the other hand the very shape of the sign conveys its meaning clearly. Thus trees, on British maps, are unmistakably deciduous or nondeciduous. On modern French maps they resemble assorted insect eggs under the microscope on the one hand, and starfish on the other, for they are shown, logically, in plan. As regards the position of objects shown by symbols in elevation it may help to remember that lighthouses, lightships, windmills, windpumps and wireless masts are so shown on ordnance maps that the correct plan position is the centre of the base of the symbol. In the case of churches the plan position is the centre of the circle (spire) or rectangle (tower) if either of these is given, but if a simple cross (with neither spire nor tower) then the plan position is the centre of the cross.

It is more important to remember the effect of scale on conventional signs than the signs themselves. At the 1-inch scale a hundredth of an inch is perceptible; but many a pencil line is much wider than this. A hundredth of an inch represents on this scale eighteen yards—many times as wide as most roads. Supposing that a road, a railway and a stream run together up a narrow valley, and pass, in it, a village with a church, it is obvious that the map must be generalized in order to fit them all in. Not only will comparative distance suffer but signs for cuttings and embankments must be made as small as possible. Roads and railways are always much wider on small-scale maps than they are in nature.

Streams, always in blue on a coloured map, are shown by a single line ("single streams" as draughtsmen call them) until they become fifteen feet wide and over.

Road classification dictates the various widths and colours on the map. At the moment, road classification is a difficult subject. On ordnance maps it depends upon personal measurement and inspection, which no other classification can be said to do, because of the prophetic element in road planning. We are so rich in good roads nowadays, however, that we may come to the point when violent colours will be used as a warning rather than a guide. Otherwise maps may become little else than records of the roads. The Ministry of Transport numbers are now given on most maps.

Woods present no difficulty on any maps. They are always shown either in green or in the symbols for individual trees. On the 1-inch ordnance map both are employed, and it is often a considerable help to rapid map-reading to be able to pick out the different types of tree. Far more important, however, is the value to those many who are professionally interested. The same may be said of the sign for "rough pasture", which is a very good guide to the amount of uncultivated ground. Parks are differently shown according as they are private or public. The public park is generally shown in a green ruling, and not a green solid like woods, whereas private parks are shown in black stipple.

Footpaths are matters of supreme importance to many. The first point to notice is that ordnance maps, by hypothesis, show what actually exists on the ground. They do not pretend to show rights of way, and are no evidence of them. Thus even if a right of way does exist, but no definite track has been made, no path will be shown. It is unfortunate that the path sign is not unlike those for some of the numerous boundaries which have also to be shown. Attention should be paid to this fact. Unfortunately footpaths were not shown on the first edition of the ordnance 1-inch (Mudge's maps).

The sea coast is almost always outlined in black, but that rule is not invariable. On ordnance maps high and low water-marks are given and submarine contours are drawn in blue. These submarine contours (an explanation of contours will follow) depend upon the soundings given on charts. They do not represent exact measurement throughout their length.

Plan conventions differ little from those described, but are all given in black. There are, however, so many abbreviations used on the plans that it will be as well to include some extracts from a conventional sign-plate. These will be found in Chapter V (on the plans). These abbreviations are not always tabulated fully in the margin. Such letters as M.R., for mooring ring, may well confuse the inexpert. Recent plans have abandoned the practice of using "shaded" or heavy lines south and east of buildings and roads, and north and west of streams. There are many old plans still in use, however, and the reason for the curious difference may be explained. For hill shadows, and indeed in every case of a supposed shadow, the light was supposed to fall from the north-west. Perhaps, at first sight, this may seem absurd considering that the sun is never there (for Great Britain). But the reason is independent of latitude or sun. It is a practical and correct acknowledgment of the fact that a man looking at a map obstructs light from his own direction (or the south), and that light does in fact tend (for right-handed people in the open or at a desk) to come from the north-west *of the map*. The north and west shading of streams was intended to suggest the shadow of the bank over the water. So far was the idea of the shadow carried, that all metalled roads (supposed to be raised and therefore to be able to cast a shadow) were shaded on the south and east, but unmetalled cart tracks were not shaded, as being strictly on ground level.

On the ordnance maps and plans you will find here and there little triangles with dots inside. These triangles represent some, but not all, of the hundred and sixty thousand odd points of the national triangulation. Each one represents a place fixed by careful instrumental measurement, and the sum total represents the skeleton, or framework, upon which all our maps depend. On the 25-inch and 6-inch plans are also given the "Bench-marks" or marked points whose exact height above mean sea level is known. These are not given on the small scale maps, but on them, every here and there, in the bottoms of valleys and on hills and passes, heights are given, usually along, or near, the roads. " Trig. Points ", represented by the triangles, control the map in plan, " Bench-marks " in height.

Supposing that all town and village names were in the same style and of the same size the map would look dreadful. On plans and maps therefore the names are carefully graded in importance and written in the style and size appropriate to the occasion. Map-lovers will notice that in the latest editions of ordnance maps the style of writing has been radically altered. The reason is partly one of taste and fashion and partly to suit modern methods of printing. All our earliest maps and plans were engraved on copper plates. The copper engraver gouged out fine little lines and dots and letters, forming V-shaped cuts into which the ink was rolled. When the paper was pressed down on the copper the ink transferred its affection to it and the map was printed. Beautifully clear and sharp these engraved maps were. But the technique of engraving and the question of holding the ink in the cut alike tended to extreme fineness. Writing became very spidery and, in the opinion of many, artificial. This same tendency led to showing houses and blocks of buildings in towns by covering them with fine parallel lines or " hatching " as it is called technically. Now that printing depends upon transferring the drawn map to stone or zinc and printing, in colour, by the thousand, names are written in bolder and better style, while houses and blocks of buildings are shown on the small scales in solid black. There is no difficulty to-day in printing large areas of black or of colour, but there *is* difficulty in printing very fine thin lines. If so be that you are interested in " alphabets ", there is a book published under the title of *Ordnance Survey Alphabets*, which is as useful in designing and painting the name of the house on the front gate, as it is in providing a model for mapping.

Maps are, however, more conventional in showing

hills than in any other way. The map is flat. One cannot build and carry a model about with one. Some conventional system has to be evolved for showing that third dimension of height, and to understand it is perhaps the only matter of real difficulty in map reading. Later on, in Chapter VIII, various systems of showing hill features are discussed, but this is obviously the place in which to deal with contours.

In the delightful island of St. Helena there is a staircase of some 600 steps leading from the back of the old Royal Engineer Office to Ladder Hill, and its barracks. Many a tourist has bitterly regretted tackling the ascent by it. Now the slope varies a little but is mainly about 45°. Let us take a section of it.

A step in building language consists of a " riser " and a "tread". The latter is, of course, what you tread on, and the former what you have to surmount. These two words express exactly the same thought as the " vertical interval " and " horizontal equivalent " of contours. The map will tell you that the " vertical interval between the contours is 50 feet ". In this case the riser is 50 feet and the " tread " or horizontal equivalent is just what the slope of the ground dictates. For example in the staircase the lower portion is steeper than the upper. The tread is only 12 inches whereas in the upper it is 15 inches. The steeper the slope the less is the distance in plan between contours. Consider the hand-rail of the staircase (which is parallel to the ground). The " gradient " of the lower portion of that hand-rail is 1/1 because the tread is equal to the riser. The gradient of the upper part is 12/15 or 4/5 or 1/1·25 because the tread is 15 inches and the riser 12 inches. The actual slope, for those whose trigonometry is sufficiently advanced, is the angle whose tangent is equal to $\dfrac{\text{riser}}{\text{tread}}$. Apply this to contours.

Supposing that another Noah's flood rose and submerged St. Helena; the governor and council having taken

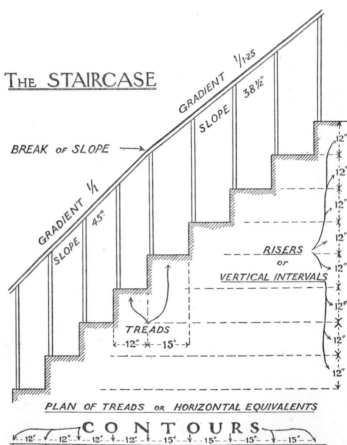

THE STAIRCASE

GRADIENT 1/1·25

SLOPE 38½°

BREAK OF SLOPE →

GRADIENT 1/1

SLOPE 45°

12"
12"
12"
12"
12"

RISERS
or
VERTICAL INTERVALS

12"
12"
12"
12"

TREADS
←--12"--*--15"--→

PLAN OF TREADS OR *HORIZONTAL EQUIVALENTS*

CONTOURS

←-12"-*-12"-*-12"-*-12"-*-15"-*-15"-*-15"-*-15"-→

Fig. 1

refuge in an ark upon Diana's Peak. Now the steps
were built by Royal Engineers; the treads are so
horizontal that the roundest marble placed upon one
would be unable to roll. Then the rising waters would
lap each step and suddenly flood its whole surface at
once. Just as they reached the edge they would mark
out all round the island a contour at the height of
that tread. Each successive 1-foot contour would be
reached in equal time however large the tread or
horizontal equivalent, for contours have a rigid caste
system—the riser or vertical interval remains constant;
each contour keeps its place and never meets its neighbours whether above or below it in the social scale,
but it may perhaps on the map. Some few miles round
the corner from the staircase in St. Helena is the
heart-shaped waterfall—a sheer cliff. On the face of
that cliff the 1-foot contours would be marked clearly,
but the map can only record the top edge of the cliff
and though every contour fits in, below or above its
neighbours, in its determination to keep its distance,
the map cannot show it.

It is a solemn thought to consider the 5 foot above
mean sea level contour which rings the twin continents
of Asia and Europe. Starting say at Calais how it
would lose all horizontal equivalents from other contours in the dock wall, how it would separate perhaps
by miles in horizontal equivalent going east and north
round the flat shores of the Baltic and the White Sea;
the cold and lengthy round to Vladivostok, the travels
far inland up Chinese rivers; along the mangrove
swamps of the south; visiting Indian ports and then,
coming back to Europe, having to go all round the Black
Sea, hoping for the best in the Gulf of Corinth, exploring
the canal system of Venice, and so by the Riviera,
Spain, and France back to join on to itself.

On modern maps contours are almost always shown
in brown. Sometimes you will find many of them
broken, to show, in figures, the height above mean sea

level. The lower margin will tell you what the vertical interval is and the horizontal equivalent depends on the country in question. In Cambridge it will be huge, in Cumberland small. In order to make the general shape more obvious it is common practice to " reinforce " or darken contours at every fourth or fifth step. American maps do this commonly, and the practice was adopted in the popular (or 4th) edition of the ordnance 1-inch of Scotland. This practice does seem to help, but goes ill with any hill shading.

The question is often asked: "What is the difference between a contour and a form line?" There is not very much. Almost all contours depend greatly upon eye sketching used to fill in the gaps between measured heights. Even the most precise measurement applies only to spots and not to the whole line. Form lines are rather sketchy contours for which the author thereof does not desire to claim too much, and they vary in correctness enormously.

A word as to conventions in colouring. Black is normally used for " detail ", by which is meant the planimetry of things solid. Occasionally, however, buildings and road margins (usually on the black plate) are shown in red. French maps often do this. Black is the most telling and significant colour of the map. Blue is always used for water whether salt or fresh. Brown is normally used for contours, and is often a reddy brown. The black, blue and brown are the colours of the simplest maps. Green is used for woods where these are shown in colour. Roads used always to be shown in burnt sienna, but, on the most modern maps, vary from red to yellow. Hill features are normally shown in sienna, and hill shading in some purplish tint. Colour is a good servant but a bad master, and the more colour applied the heavier must names and lines become.

CHAPTER IV

Map Projections

SINCE the earth is a sphere it is obviously impossible to map it entirely satisfactorily on a flat piece of paper. Nothing, in fact, but a globe can be used for an accurate picture, showing each portion in its correct relative shape and size. Globes are not articles to multiply about the house, however, and offer little chance of showing things at a scale large enough to serve normal purposes. For example a globe on which the world was mapped at one inch to the mile would have a diameter of well over 200 yards.

For that reason a great variety of methods of showing a spherical surface on a plane (the flat paper) have been evolved. All these methods are called map projections. The word projection does not imply that the methods in question have any necessary connexion with geometry or perspective. There are some map projections which do presuppose an image thrown on a screen by a light inside or outside the spherical earth, but they are few and unimportant. Some of the methods are geometrical, some are conventional, a few perspective, and some can only be described as fanciful. Each and all are map projections so long as they provide definite and orderly ways of calculating dimensions and directions and of plotting them on paper. One further thought is necessary before beginning a description of these methods. The land surface of the earth is not all at mean sea level. It is true that

mountains are small in comparison with the earth's
size. For example Mount Everest would stick out from
the globe for 1-inch mapping (diam. 220 yards) by
less than 6 inches. All such irregularities are neglected on
maps except in so far as they are shown by contours,
hachures or layers. The sphere of the earth for which
map projections have been evolved is taken to be the
mean surface of the sea. To get the mental picture
right one must imagine seas and oceans to meet through
a series of canals driven across the continents. Everything is mapped as if it were on the level of the water in
these canals. Fields, half-way up Ben Nevis or Snowdon,
are not shown, nor are their areas given on the plans,
as they actually are, but as they would be if they
were squashed down on to the spherical surface as
defined by these canals.

The practical effect of flattening out this spherical
surface itself, of putting the world through a mangle,
must be to distort shapes, and to alter bearings and
scales. The distortion will vary enormously with the
amount of country which is to be mapped. Think of
a globe of about 2 feet in diameter, and pin upon it a
piece of paper sufficiently large to include, at the correct
scale, the outline of the whole of Great Britain. The
piece of paper would be no longer than $1\frac{1}{2}$ inches, and
half that width. It would nearly, but not quite, lie flat
on a 2-foot globe, without crumpling. But the area enclosed in a 25-inch plan is no more than $1\frac{1}{2}$ square miles.
On the 2-foot globe this area would be too small to see.
There would be no distortion between the globe and the
flat paper, and map projections, in such a case, lose all
significance. A 1-inch map shows an area of about 700
square miles. Even this area is too small to show any
sensible difference between most ordinary projections.
On the other hand each 1-inch sheet has to join correctly
on to all surrounding sheets and the process has to
go on till all Great Britain is covered. But now we
are considering an area so comparatively large as to

make distortion between sphere and plane noticeable.
It is beginning to be a matter of importance which
projection is chosen. Think of larger and larger areas
until we get a hemisphere and then the whole world.
It is impossible to fit flat paper on to it without innumerable cuts or innumerable distortions. It is
for the above reasons that the English land surveyors
of the past were able to ignore the subject. Their
surveys were too small in area to make the projection
of any consequence, and, in fact, they behaved as if
the world were flat.

Meridians and Parallels.

It is difficult to discuss projections without talking
of meridians, parallels, poles, and great circles, and a
few words may well be devoted to them. The north
and south poles are the opposite extremities of the
axis round which the earth rotates. The equator is a
circle drawn round the earth so that each point upon
it is equidistant from north and south poles. A clean
cut through the earth at the equator would divide
it into two equal parts, and pass through its centre.
The equator is therefore a great circle. A meridian
is a great circle at right angles to the equator, and
therefore passes through the poles. Over the meridian
of any particular place the sun passes when it is noon
at that place. There are just as many meridians as
one cares to draw, but, as the equator is divided into
360 degrees, with the zero point, as far as we are concerned, where the Greenwich meridian cuts it, we can
think of 360 meridians spaced a degree from each other
on the equator. Incidentally one-sixtieth of each degree
space on the equator—a minute of longitude—is a
geographical mile, and is 6087·2 feet.

Meridians are also divided into 360 degrees; and a
quarter, or 90 degrees, is the distance between the
equator (0) and one or other of the poles (90°). These
degrees are numbered from a zero point on the equator

and the latitude of any place is the distance (or number of degrees) measured from the equator northwards or southwards (according to whether the place is in the northern or southern hemispheres) along the meridian of that place.

Think of any number of points at the latitude (N.) of London, and consider a cut through the earth passing through all these points. Such a cut would not divide the world into two equal parts. That north of London would be much the smaller of the two. The cut is, of course, a small circle, does not pass through the centre of the earth, and is distinctly smaller in diameter than the equator. Such a circle is called a parallel of latitude. One further thought. Take any two points on a meridian, and draw through them great circles at right angles to that meridian round the earth. By definition cuts through these great circles must include the centre of the earth. At whatever distance from each other they may be on the initial meridian they will get nearer and nearer to each other, cut each other 90° away on the equator, cross, cut each other again, and come back to their starting points. These great circles at right angles to a meridian have nothing to do with latitude or longitude but a great deal to do with projections.

The Cage.

Let us return to meridians and parallels, and consider the earth to be replaced by a wire cage composed of them (see fig. 2). Any portion of that cage is called a graticule, a word which it will be convenient to use later on. Any individual hole in the graticule, including the elements of meridians and parallels by which it is bounded, will be called a mesh. The wire cage will be considered instead of the earth, because if meridians and parallels are once mapped the remainder of the map can easily be fitted to them.

Cylindrical Projections.

First of all, then, take the cage and cut all the meridians where they cross each other at the north and south poles. Next, consider all the parallels to be made of elastic wire which will expand as required. Pull out the tops of the meridians until they stand as vertical rods north and south of the equator. The

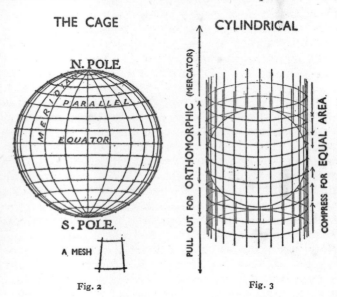

Fig. 2   Fig. 3

result will be a cylinder of these meridian wires, the parallels all now having been forced outwards till they are equal in diameter to the equator. Each individual mesh will be a square. Now snip all the parallels on the same meridian line and lay the result out flat. The projection so formed is called a *cylindrical* (the equidistant cylindrical), and no maps of any importance are drawn upon this pure cylindrical.

Almost every form of projection can be modified to fall into one or the other of the two groups—" *orthomorphic* " (or "*conformal*") on the one hand, "*equal area*" on the other. The words orthomorphic and conformal, Greek and Latin respectively in origin, imply true to shape, which is as much as to say that the distortions (present in every projection) leave the scale, in this case, the same in all directions round a point. The scale is not the same all over the map, but it is so locally. "Equal area ", on the other hand, means that all over the map differences of area on the ground are represented by similar differences of area on the paper.

Let us get back to the cylindrical and see how this works out. To make our cage, pulled out into cylindrical form, " equal area ", we shall have to make the meridian rods compressible. The parallels have all been greatly lengthened, whilst the meridians remain the same length. In any one mesh the area is too large, therefore, and the farther north the mesh the more is the scale enlarged. Lay weights over the top of all meridians wires so as to compress them and consider that they are the more compressible the farther you are from the equator and the nearer you are to the poles. Then press until the area of each mesh is the same as that of the similar mesh of the original cage. The result is an " equal area cylindrical ".

Now turn the original cylindrical into an orthomorphic. To keep shape and scale true round a point we must enlarge or diminish meridians and parallels by the same amounts. But the ordinary cylindrical has increased the lengths of every parallel, and the increase grows with the latitude. Consider the meridians to be also elastic, the elasticity growing with the latitude. Now pull the meridians upwards and downwards from the equator. The cylinder will now be many times as tall as it was before [1] but it has become orthomorphic and it has become the *Mercator*.

As a result Iceland is shown five and a half times as large as it would have been if it were on the equator.

---

[1] Actually it reaches infinity.

Greenland assumes the same size as India. England is three times its proper size. The arctic regions dominate the picture and India shrinks to insignificance compared to Siberia. For maps on or close to the equator The Mercator is a perfectly good projection. The War Office has produced an excellent map of the Celebes (on the air route between Sumatra and Australia) on it.

For more general maps, those of the world for example, its only merits are simplicity of construction and rectangular shape. For the sailor, however, it has great advantages, because any compass bearing can be drawn across the world and remain the same bearing all the way. It is, in fact, a projection designed for navigation and charts. As the scale changes rapidly with increasing latitude, charts (of any considerable area) cannot be considered to have any but a " mean " scale.

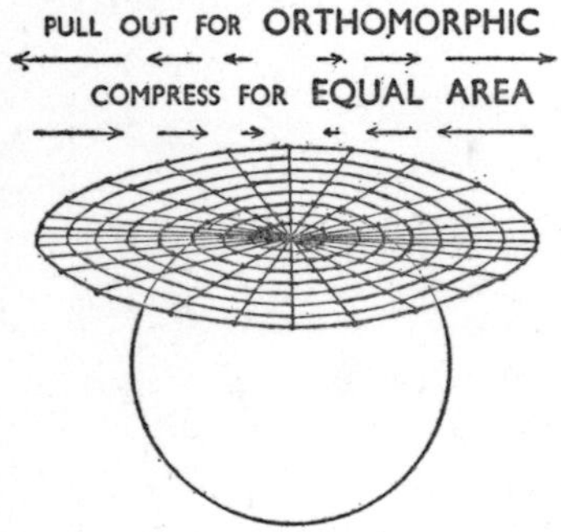

PULL OUT FOR **ORGHOMORPHIC**

COMPRESS FOR **EQUAL AREA**

ZENITHAL

or AZIMUTHAL

Fig. 4

Zenithal Projections.

Let us help India to its revenge on the Mercator. Take the original cage and divide it into two halves by cutting round the equator. The result will be two hemispherical affairs like fly-proof dish covers. Take one and put it on a table. Consider all its parallels elastic as before. Pull the equator circle outwards horizontally, expanding all the parallels till the meridians ease down to the table and lie flat. We have now got a *zenithal* (alternatively *azimuthal*) projection. It is, however, neither orthomorphic nor equal area as yet, and India is still unavenged. It is called the zenithal equidistant. Obviously the parallels have been expanded most near the equator, least near the north pole. Make meridians also elastic (the more so as they approach the equator) and pull some more, till the scale is the same in all directions in each mesh. This is the orthomorphic zenithal and on it an enormous India would have its own back on Siberia. To make an equal area zenithal would, of course, imply firstly pulling the dish cover flat on the table and then compressing the meridians most near the equator, least nearest the poles. An equal area zenithal makes a good hemispherical map if the centre is shifted from the pole on to the equator. Zenithal projections are also used for star charts. They are very useful for polar maps and in the orthomorphic form (called the *stereographic*) are used sometimes for islands. In that case, however, the " zenith " is taken in some central position of the area (which becomes the apex of the dish cover).

Conical Projections.

In Great Britain we are all familiar with a storm cone. Convert the cage into one by pulling outwards simultaneously on the poles and on the equator. Let everything be elastic, in fact, except the parallels of latitude 45° north and south. We may imagine an astonished earth remaining spherically inside held in position by these two parallels. The result is two conical projections, one of the northern and the other of the southern hemisphere. Cut again through the equator, and taking the northern half cut the equator just beside a meridian and snip all the parallels at the same meridian till you come to the north pole. Then lay the result flat on the table. It is a conical projection of the northern hemisphere " with one standard parallel " (i.e. that of 45° north). Cones may be of many kinds. The dunce's cap is a tall affair and if such a cone were fitted on the earth the standard parallel (the rigid one which remains true to scale) might be as far south (say) as Cairo. On the other hand the Chinese form of straw hat is wide and shallow.

The standard parallel might run through Spitzbergen. Hats, as well we know, may be worn on the side of the head. So may conical projections, although, as a rule, they prefer the button on the top to represent the north or south pole.

Two Standard Parallels.

Now for a modification of the three main varieties already discussed. Need the cylinder touch the earth round the equator? Take the cylinder and compress it in circumference (making all parallels equally compressible). Think of the top of the cylinder as sharp enough to slice off a portion of the earth. Put the earth on top and push it down from the top to the centre. The sharpened top may be supposed to have sliced off a belt near the equator. Then two parallels (where the earth was cut) would become " standard " (say 30° north and south).

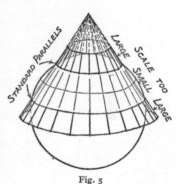

CONICAL

WITH TWO STANDARD PARALLELS

Fig. 5

Where the earth was cut off it was too big (i.e. the scale of the projection is too small). Where, on the other hand, the earth lies, still, inside the cylinder, the latter is too big (i.e. the scale of the projection is too big).

Obviously the same measures can be taken with the zenithal and conical (see fig. 5). The plane of the zenithal can be pushed through the earth (say at latitude 80° north) having a standard parallel (of 80) on which the scale is correct (instead of being correct only at the pole itself). The projecting north polar area (from 80° to 90°) will be shown too small on the projection and lower latitudes will be shown too large.

Similarly with the conical, suppose it pushed through the earth leaving a projecting band of the latter outside. We can now have two standard parallels (say at 40° and 50° north). This business of getting a bit of the earth outside is useful because it spreads the unavoidable distortions of projections over a wider area. To return to the conical, remember that it can be made orthomorphic by pulling out the meridians where the parallels arc too big (i.e. where they are outside the earth) and compressing them where the parallels are too small (i.e. inside the earth). The *conical orthomorphic* with two standard parallels is "Lambert's second", and a most useful projection. Naturally since the scale is correct all the way on two parallels (and not up and down the meridian), such a projection is best for a country (or continent) which extends east and west but not much north and south. Supposing Crete was twenty times its present size, it would form an ideal subject for the conical orthomorphic. Czecho-Slovakia would go well upon it. That admirable series, the War Office 1/4M of Asia, is upon it.

There are also quite a few conical equal area projections, of which Bonne's is, for us, the most important, since the Scottish 1-inch ordnance map was, for long, drawn upon it (although it is so no longer). Before describing it, however, let us remember that the stresses and strains in the " cage ", with all the compressions and expansions we have given it, are rather involved, and may result in pulling meridians a bit out of the straight, parallels a little out of the circular. Let us remember, too, that the cartographer is not usually mapping the world, or even continents. He does not require all the cage, even when it has been pulled and pushed to his liking. He will cut out of cylinder, plane, or cone just that part suited to his purpose and will naturally see to it that his standard parallels are chosen for that part. Bonne's projection (also used for the 1/80,000 of France) cuts out a portion of a " conical with one standard parallel". Where the central meridian and the standard parallel cross is the "origin". Having smoothed out his portion he sees that each parallel (they are all concentric) is at its proper distance from its neighbours up and down his central meridian. Then out along his parallels he measures distances correct to where the next meridian should be, and the next, and so on, and then joins up these points to form the meridians. Obviously one cannot have one's cake and eat it. If the scale is everywhere correct on the parallels and on the central meridian, the other meridians must suffer, and they become, in fact, curves. This projection is equal area, for what that is worth. For the 1-inch of Scotland it is worth little. For those who are mathematically interested the origin of the old Scottish Bonne was at latitude 57° 30' (north) and longitude 4° 00' (west) and the radius of the standard parallel was 13361612·2 feet.

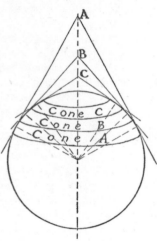

Fig. 6.—The Polyconic Idea

The Polyconic.

The Polyconic projection introduces an interesting modification. Consider the fly-proof dish cover. First of all pull it out till the dunce's cap is formed, with a standard parallel (say) at 10° north. Then press the top down again a little (keeping the 10° parallel fixed). You have flattened the slope a bit. Now fix the parallel of 20° north and press the top down a bit more. Fix the 30° parallel and repeat the pressing and fixing. The cage now becomes a tier of conical segments getting flatter and flatter as you go north (or south). In actual

practice each segment is generally a degree. When
it is cut up along a meridian and smoothed out, the
circles which represent parallels are not concentric,
but are functions of their own latitudes, and the meridians are curved except for the central one. Topographical maps of the United States of America are
polyconic. In the *rectangular polyconic* the curved
meridians are made to cut the parallels at right angles,
by sacrificing scale along the parallels.

The Transverse Mercator and the Cassini.

Let us now get back to the cage of meridians and
parallels again and stand it up on a table so that the
axis is vertical and the north pole is on top. Pick it up
again and turn it half over so that the axis is horizontal,
and north and south poles are at the same distance
away from the table. The equator now rings the earth
in the same way as one of the meridians did when the
cage was upright, and one of the meridians has taken its
place as equator. Let the old equator now be the Greenwich meridian, and all the old meridians are now great
circles perpendicular to the Greenwich meridian. The
present top of the cage becomes the north pole, and the
old parallels of latitude become small circles parallel to
the Greenwich meridian. Take a point on the Greenwich meridian about 52° north of the (new) equator,
and find the great circle (at right angles to the Greenwich meridian) nearest to that point. Where these
two cut will be well inside England and we can consider
the projection of the first general ordnance 1-inch
map of England. We have found an origin for it. (The
real one was in Delamere Forest at latitude 53° 13'
17.274" north, and longitude 2° 41' 03.562" west of
Greenwich.) Next, snip out a portion of the cage from
50° to 56° north, and from 6° west to 2° east. Lay it
on the table just as it is, the meridian humped up in the
middle and the great circles tending to get nearer to
each other the farther they are from the meridian.

This meridian and these great circles are the rectangular co-ordinates of the earlier ordnance survey small scales. Any point to be plotted on the map is known as lying on a great circle perpendicular to the central meridian and at such and such a distance from it, and at such and such a distance up the meridian from the origin. Now squash the snippet flat on to the table. The meridian loses its hump, the great circles become just ordinary lines parallel to each other and at right angles to the meridian. That is how the co-ordinates are plotted and that is the *Cassini Projection*.

It will be remembered that when the cage was turned over by 90° the old parallels became small circles parallel to the Greenwich meridian. These now become just straight lines all parallel to each other and to the meridian. The straightened out great circles and the old parallels, now lines parallel to the meridian, are the " sheet lines ", or are parallel to the sheet lines, of ordnance small-scale maps.

Look back at the cylinder to which we stretched the cage when the cylindrical projection was in the making. The Cassini is just the same as the bit of the cylindrical projection nearest to the equator, only it has been turned at right angles. The cylinder now lies upon its side, instead of standing erect. We made that cylinder orthomorphic by pulling out the upright meridians. We can now make the Cassini orthomorphic by pulling out the great circles. If we do we get the *Transverse mercator* (known also as the *Gauss Conformal*) which is the projection of the new 1-inch (and smaller scale) ordnance maps. It is nothing but a Mercator at right angles, and its use is very common.

The Cassini projection obviously distorts in the same way as a cylindrical. The lines at right angles to the meridian ought to be meeting each other and instead are plotted as parallel. Therefore, when you get far from the central meridian, distances north and south seem larger than they ought to be, and that error, on the 1-inch of England, amounted (in the extreme case at 175 miles east of the meridian) to five feet in a mile. The plans (large scales) were not plotted from one single meridian because their large scale would have made such an error noticeable. They were all plotted from county meridians.

The change from the Cassini to the Transverse Mercator for the small scales will not affect ordinary map users. It will make fresh surveying easier, and it was no bother to do. Instead, however, of being an ordinary transverse mercator that now adopted for ordnance maps cuts through the earth, and is correct to scale on lines parallel to the central meridian and 200,000 yards from it (east and west). The origin is where the meridian of 2° west crosses the parallel of latitude 49° north. The extreme errors at the easternmost part of East Anglia are about 2 feet in a mile.

The Cassini and Transverse Mercator are good projections so long as they do not extend too far east and west. North and south they can go on all round the world, and this is an example of how projections are cut out of the cage in small bits or in complete bandeaux. It is therefore difficult to find a projection to cover all the maps of a continent (such as North America) large in every direction. Where a very large area is covered by a series of maps, these latter are generally on a projection which is natural to each sheet and not to the series as a whole. The earth may be considered to have been cut, like a diamond, into innumerable facets, each of which becomes one map sheet on its own projection. In these cases the maps are not rectangular like our British maps, but are bounded east and west by meridians which converge to the north or south pole, and, north and south, by bits of circles representing parallels of latitude. If the map is north of the equator then its north margin is shorter than its southern one; the opposite applying south of the equator.

The International one-in-a-million map is a case in point. Some day its sheets will cover all the land surface of the globe. Each sheet is plotted on a *rectified polyconic*. The polyconic has been described before, and the rectification consists of making the scale true on two separate meridians 2° removed (east and west) from the central meridian, whilst it is also true on the north and south bounding parallels. Nothing better could have been chosen, but of course the sheets will not fit together except in the form of a cross. North and south each sheet fits on its neighbours, and east and west it will do the same, but the corner sheets will then not fit in. This same projection is used for the 1/2M of Africa—a splendid War Office series.

The Polyhedric.

Another " single sheet " projection is the *Polyhedric* which is most common on the Continent. Out of the cage cut one single mesh. Flatten it out and pull the parallels straight. The result is a four-sided figure, the meridians, east and west, of equal length, and the parallel nearest the pole being shorter than that farthest from the pole. It is used for the German 1/100,000.

Miscellaneous.

The time is now ripe for thinking of some of the odder projections. We will start with the *gnomonic*, so called because it is the projection used on a sundial (or gnomon). This is a perspective projection and the eye (or source of light) is supposed to be inside the cage and at its centre. Obviously the whole globe cannot be projected on one sheet, and the distortion even for a small area is great. It has the property, however, of making all great circles straight lines. Great circle sailing, or flying, is naturally important because the shortest distance between any two ports (say Southampton and New York) is along the great circle on which both lie. On the other hand compass bearings are not straight lines on the gnomonic, so that the advantage is more than offset by the drawback.

In the middle of last century the Ordnance Survey was inventing, or defining, something new every day. Lime light and zincography were two of the inventions. The odd European standard bars (such as toises and klafters) of that day were all compared with each other, and the lengths of the royal and common cubit (the old Egyptian standards of length) were defined. Naturally map projections were not forgotten. Colonel A. R. Clarke, England's most famous geodesist, calculated and described the *general minimum error perspective*. This was not one particular projection but a method of calculating the distance of the perspective centre (or source of light) such that the resulting errors should be a minimum for any given area. Sir Henry James, who reigned for twenty-one years as Director-General, then had the particular case of the main land surface of the globe investigated. Taking the centre of his map surface at 15° east and 23½° north, and covering a radius of the sphere of 113½°, he places the source of light at 1·367 times the radius of the earth from its centre (or 2·367 times the radius from his map centre). The maps were plotted and published, and are to be seen at the Ordnance Survey.

Then there comes the *orthographic* perspective, in which the source of light, infinitely removed, sends parallel rays of light on to the cage perpendicular to the map surface. The distortion of this projection is very great and hence it is practically never used.

Among the more useful odd projections is one invented by the German Professor *Mollweide*. It shows the whole earth on a single sheet of paper. In form it is elliptical. The parallels are all straight lines, and the meridians are ellipses. Its advantage is that its distortions are smaller than those of the world mercator, and it can be turned round to make a *transverse Mollweide* which gives just as good a picture.

The earth can be shown in all sorts of other odd ways and shapes which cannot be gone into here, but which the mathematically minded will revel in. New projections can be invented to show any property of the cage which you are interested in. For example, a projection may be drawn such that all distances from two points, say London and New York, will be true to scale (but distances from other points will not be true to scale).

Practically one must remember that for such scales as the 1-inch almost any reasonable projection will be sensibly correct as far as the limits of each particular sheet extend. The problem for the national carto-grapher is to find a projection which will hold good over his country, and his difficulties are small compared with those of the atlas map-maker who has to deal with areas so much vaster.

To go deeper into the subject see *Map Projections* by A. R. Hinks, Cambridge University Press. 12*s*. 6*d*.

CHAPTER V

Plans

Old Plans.

IT is only of comparatively recent years that the public has been able to buy plans, and to be certain that all of them are made and published on a common principle. A hundred and fifty years ago neighbouring towns or villages or properties might have had plans, but they would have differed markedly in scale and appearance. One, for example, might have been at a scale of two chains to the inch, another at forty-four feet to the inch. One might be highly coloured, with coats of arms all round the margin and a long dedication to some patron, whilst the other, on sheepskin, might stick to business and black ink. Moreover, these plans would rarely, if ever, join up properly even if brought to the same scale, and, remaining unpublished, were not at the service of any save the employer. They are of immense national interest as records of English life, development and history. They are, however, not the theme of this chapter, which deals with the plans published and available for the public.

Beginnings of the Ordnance Survey.

Even the State department, the Ordnance Survey, did not begin plan-making on any general scheme. The first duty of the Ordnance Survey was to make a 1-inch map, and other duties continued to be thrust upon it in proportion as national necessities forced the hands of a careful Treasury. It was in 1841 that official large town plans were first found necessary for the civil community. The very sketchy drainage and water systems of that period had resulted in an outbreak of cholera some ten years previously. Something had to be done about it. The Ordnance Survey was called in, took innumerable levels (even in cellars and basements) drew plans of the most intimate nature at scales of 10 feet and 24 inches to the mile, in the thicker and opener parts respectively, and sent the completed drawings to the local authorities, who, one hopes, guard them as most valuable records. It was upon these plans that more adequate drainage was designed and installed. Each of these town series, however, was independent of its neighbour. Each had its own "north point", independent of any general system of sheets, and none of them were published.

The "Health of Towns" plans referred to above were not primarily "property" or "cadastral" surveys. The word cadastral comes from the Latin "capitastrum", according to the learned, and implies a connexion with taxation or valuation. It was in relation to these matters that the 6-inch survey of Ireland was made, starting in 1824. That country was suffering from very unequal taxation and both measurements and plans were absurdly inadequate. Look, for example, at the names of the units of land and measurement in vogue. "Townlands, ploughlands, colps, greeves, bullibos, bullibellas, cartrons, tates, horsemen, beds". As the Commission which deliberated on the subject remarked, "They are at this day manifestly unequal both in quantity and value, being made on grounds that are all obsolete and antiquated." So it was in Ireland that Government plans were first made and published, and from 1824 to 1840 the greater part of the Ordnance Survey staff was concentrated there.

It is curious that a scale of six inches to a mile should have been considered large enough, since small individual properties cannot be well shown, and their sizes on paper were too small for reasonable accuracy in measuring areas. The fact was, however, that the areas of townlands and not of single fields were the important factor. Some half-dozen townlands went to the parish, and their areas were calculated from field measurement and not derived (as on our present 25-inch) from paper measurement on the completed plan. Later on, the 6-inch was found too small and Ireland was surveyed on the larger scale (25-inch). The original 6-inch survey, under the singularly capable direction of General Colby, was responsible for several interesting things. The limelight was invented by Captain Drummond (later to be Under-Secretary of State for Ireland) during its course, official British contouring began there, and the memoirs which accompanied the completed survey of each county were models of their kind. Each Irish county had its separate meridian and separate series of plans, and these were beautifully engraved.

Meanwhile, in England, the industrial revolution was in full swing, railways were calling for survey, tithe questions were active, and surveyors were earning " 5 and 10 guineas a day ". It was in fact the heyday of private land surveying. Some of it was good, but naturally reflected both the expense, and the variability, of independent and uncorrelated work. As was stated before a Royal Commission the cost of these private surveys ultimately fell " as a heavy tax on the whole country ". Naturally the position had to grow pretty difficult before we made up our minds to do the job properly. The discussions which followed in the House, and between departments, are known, in the annals of the Survey, as " the Battle of the Scales ". Was a survey to be made on a large scale? and if so what should it be? The decision to make a large-scale survey was undoubtedly influenced by Napoleon's cadastrals. These plans were made at the direction of each French " commune " (the equivalent of a parish) but were all at the scale of 1/2500. The survey was a simple one with the chain, unhelped (generally) by triangulation, and each commune had an index to its individual plans or " parcellaires " on the scale of 1/10,000 (very nearly six inches to the mile). These indexes (oddly enough) underlie all the topographical work of the French 1/80,000 map (and its derivatives the 1/200,000 and 1/500,000). In 1858 there was an international conference on cadastral surveying at Brussels. British delegates attended and agreed that the scale of 1/2500 was suitable, and so, after further discussion at home, the decimal scale of 1/2500 was adopted. By this time, however, we had surveyed a good many parts on scales derived from our own units. Thus the scales of 5 and 10 feet to the mile (1/1056 and 1/528) were being used in towns, and the 6-inch area (1/10,560) was growing rapidly. However the decimal or " natural " was adopted for the larger scales but the 6-inch had already become too valuable in national records to alter. It is doubtful if the scale of 1/2500 would have carried the day for the larger scale if it had not been so very nearly 25 inches to the mile (25·344 inches to the mile), or, much more important, if an acre was not so very nearly 1 square inch (1·0018 of an inch) upon it. " Any carpenter could do it," said General Sir Henry James, commenting on the simplicity of acres and square inches, and thinking obviously of pencils and set squares. We made the best of both worlds, then, but we still talk of 25-inch plans and still, also, of the 5 and 10-foot town plans, although the latter of these became 1/500 (instead of 1/528). Fortunately, however, we kept to our own ideas as to survey. Our plans are based upon a common triangulation and levelling, are published in definite sheet lines, and include a mass of information for the engineer, the administrative authority, the lawyer, and the private individual. The French plans are in manuscript and give little else than property boundaries. Yet the cost to the state was roughly the same in both cases.

A Real Start on the Plans.

The decision to survey all cultivated country on the 25-inch, leaving the 6-inch unsupported in remoter and uncultivated parts, was not made till 1858. Plans already made (mostly of important military areas) were gradually gathered into the new survey but have left their records, fortunately, behind them.

The Town Plans.

The first town plans on the true 5- and 10-foot to the mile scale were all engraved. They show an extraordinary wealth of detail. The minutest item of garden paths and beds, the exact position of trees, and the inside plan of churches appeared upon them. We shall not see such beautiful plan work again until we have a technique of cheap printing which will equal that from copper. Later on the programme of town surveying continued under the new system and, published by lithography, covered every town of over 4000 inhabitants. In 1892 it was about time to think of beginning revision and republication of these town plans, when it was decided to abandon them as a state duty, and to leave them in the hands of local authorities. Some day, however, they will be revived, for as land registration spreads reliable and official maps must be made to support it.

The 25-inch.

Meantime the 25-inch plans, now the largest state scale, were finished. There are over 50,000 of them. It will be of interest to consider some of the matters they show. Before the 25-inch, boundaries between county and county, parish and parish, were not generally known to the public and not plotted on any but the tithe maps. They were periodically perambulated or " beaten ", and the authorities were certain old men who had repeated the ceremonies for many years.

These ancients, "the fit and proper persons", the Ordnance Survey was empowered to call upon, and as the boundaries were described by them, in the field, the surveyor mapped them. Nowadays the final authority on administrative boundaries and modifications thereof is the Minister of Health, and of course any change is recorded and corrected on the next edition of the plan. There are some curious points in connexion with sea-shore boundaries. In England and Wales high and low water marks are adjudged to be those of an ordinary or average tide, whereas in Scotland ancient custom relies on mean spring tides. On a Scottish plan the abbreviation H.W.M.O.S.T. means High Water Mark of Ordinary Spring Tides, whereas in England and Wales the S. (for spring) is omitted. These lines are important because parish boundaries go down to low water mark. High and low water marks are not exactly at a continuous level round the coasts of Great Britain, because shapes of inlets, winds, tides, and currents, have their influence. They have to be surveyed in situ, therefore, and in the good old days surveyors drew a " mud and water allowance " in virtue of the circumstances of this difficult survey. If you are interested in rural districts, urban districts, municipal boroughs, and county boroughs (all aggregates of the parish), in parliamentary county divisions and parliamentary boroughs, or perhaps in catchment areas, you will find them recorded on the plans or on the " half-inch county administrative diagrams ".

Turning from administrative to private boundaries we find quite a different story. The only man who seems quite positive as to the ownership of a party fence or wall is our neighbour who wishes either to get it repaired as cheaply as possible or else to forbid our putting a lean-to shed against it. It is odd how often ownership changes hands. The plans do not record property boundaries except along parish and county boundaries. The terms of reference of the

government survey include material boundaries but
not boundaries of properties. Talking of private
properties leads on to the question of land registration.
Under present arrangements there are certain areas
(the County of London is one) in which land registration is compulsory on any alteration of ownership and
thereafter continues. An Order in Council can make
any county or portion of a county a "compulsory
area". There are also many voluntary registrations.
All registrations, compulsory or voluntary, require a
corresponding plan. In London, for example, the
plan in question is one on the 5-foot scale (1/1056) and
so the old plans of London will soon be on sale again.

On the 25-inch plans each field or "parcel" has its
serial number. These numbers started because there
used to be a book for each parish in which the areas were
given (and, incidentally, a description of the use to
which the parcel was put). The serial numbers cross
referenced from book to plan, and also, of course,
assisted an orderly system of measuring and checking.
Nowadays these serial numbers are in constant use in
estate management, because they give each parcel
a definite and individual tally. Below the serial number
is given the area. As already mentioned above, however, the area is that enclosed by material boundaries
and not necessarily by property boundaries. All
areas are measured whether they refer to private or
public ownership. The first survey abstracted the
figures throughout Great Britain under headings (a)
land, (b) water, (c) saltmarsh, (d) foreshore, (e) tidal
water. Nowadays a much more detailed analysis is
called for, and includes woods and forests, public parks,
recreation grounds, mountain, heath, and moorland.
These are the figures used by Departments of State
in all relevant discussions.

Owners may find inconvenience from a change of
serial number affecting one, or several, parcels in which
they are interested. Changes are bound to occur in

a countryside which alters so much, but any old numbers which have dropped out (built over, for example)
are recorded in the top margin of the plan. The War
and its aftermath of hard times has affected the pace
of revision a great deal and restricted it (for a time)
to parts of urgent importance. Areas are computed
afresh on those newly revised plans, but not on neighbouring plans which have not been revised. Consequently, a parcel (say 91), lying in two plans and divided
by the sheet line, has not (in such cases) the full area
stamped under it, but only that part which lies in the
sheet in question. Moreover, even the serial number
may bc changed on the revised plan and not on the
unrevised. These bothers are part of the price of economy. Areas of parcels are given only on the 25-inch
scale and not on either the town plans or the 6-inch.

The names on the 25-inch are the outcome of a very
thorough system of inquiries and checks. There are
two name books which reappear in every revision—
the Parish, and the Object, name book. The proper
authorities are visited, their opinions logged, and
decision made. The principle followed is that of local
custom, but there is no doubt that some eighty years
of this work has tended to safeguard continuity.
Our ancestors regarded spelling as a matter of little
importance. In the original compilation of the name
books it was a matter of the greatest difficulty to
secure agreement. Of one parish it is recorded that
three different parties insisted on spelling the parish
name in different ways.

Antiquities.

During the years of the first 1-inch map, from 1784
to 1850 roughly, the survey on the ground was at the
2-inch scale. It was in these days that the mapping
of antiquities began. General William Roy, post office
official, soldier, historian, antiquarian, geodesist,
" Surveyor-General of the Coasts " and Fellow of the

Royal Society, had been the most active in the making
of that map of the Highlands (after the '45 rebellion)
which is always known by his name. In spirit, though
not in fact, he was the father of the Ordnance Survey,
and much of his mentality colours its earliest history.
It is no wonder that the author of *The Military Antiquities of the Romans in Great Britain* should have
passed on his interest in such matters to his successors.
Much of the greatest archæological importance was
recorded in these early days, but, naturally, the larger
opportunities of the 25-inch made an adequate record
much more possible.   For many years the duty of
finding and mapping sites of archæological interest
fell upon the officers and men engaged on surveying
or revising.   On the whole the work was well done,
but archæology has advanced beyond the power of
anyone who has not studied it professionally to follow.
In recent years a special archæological officer superin-
tends, inspects, and prevents the inclusion of incorrect
names and descriptions.   Antiquities are recorded on
the plan as under:

> Prehistoric *(Prior to A.D. 43.)*
> ROMAN *(A.D. 43 to A.D. 420)*
> Saxon & Mediæval *(A.D. 420 to A.D. 1688.)*

The investigations and inspections necessary for the
proper record on the 25-inch are making it possible to
publish various epoch maps—Roman Britain, Darkest
England, and Seventeenth-century England, for example, which will be dealt with later on.   Air-photo-
graphs have been of the greatest value in the discovery
of Roman and prehistoric sites.

Contours and Bench-marks.

Contours, a hundred years ago, were still a newish
thought in Great Britain.   Doctor Charles Hutton,
who was measuring the amount of solid matter in

Schiehallion for his investigation on density and attraction, contoured that mountain in 1777. He " fell on the idea ", as he says. For our national surveys the beginning was in Ireland and there too Colby "fell on the idea " in 1830. The construction of roads and railways, which naturally follow the best graded lines (or those as near to the horizontal as possible), seems to have forced him to this conclusion. From that date, with the blessing of Parliamentary and other committees, contouring became universal on the 6-inch and upon all smaller scales. The 25-inch and the town plans were never contoured. Indeed official decision was against it, but provided for a large number of bench-marks and spot heights instead. Bench-marks, shown by a broad arrow, and the letters B.M. give the height to the second place of decimals of a foot. Spot or surface heights are to the nearest foot only. It is a pity in some ways that no contours are given, because, no matter what the scale may be, even a single contour " orients " one in height and gives the lie of the land, as no number of scattered heights can.

Now a word of warning. A system of spirit levelling must start from some point the height of which is known or assumed. In the early days the survey datum was a point on a dock wall at Liverpool. Obviously this was not a very happy choice. Lying in a tidal river, the old datum was not likely to witness, with sufficient accuracy, to mean sea level. The first levelling system, completed and published in 1861, rested, therefore, on an unsatisfactory datum and had in addition small errors (at any rate very small for those days) which began to be suspected early in this century. A new levelling has now been completed between the carefully chosen tidal stations of Newlyn and Dunbar. But it takes time to relevel all the minor lines and to revise the values of those bench-marks which are but a mile and a half or so from each other all over the face of the land. Consequently the plans are now in a transition stage. The difference between the values of the earlier and later levellings is not constant but varies (within small limits) from sheet to sheet. Anyone using bench-mark heights must look in the bottom margin to see whether the Newlyn or the Liverpool datum governs the values given. Either is entirely satisfactory as a basis for local work, but it is not wise to mix them.

The 6-inch is contoured, sometimes in blue and sometimes in red, but only the more accurately surveyed contours are shown. For the greater part of the country these are the 50, 100, and by 100's to 1000 feet (above mean sea level). In Scotland and the north of England the 25-foot contour is often also surveyed, and the heights above 1000 feet are usually contoured at intervals of 250 feet. The 1-inch shows many more contours, as will presently be described, but it was held unwise to include any but the most accurate contouring on the plans. The "lake bed" contours of most English and Scottish lakes are also given. They depend upon soundings and could not, naturally, be surveyed in the ordinary way. The intervals at which these contours are shown varies, and the Scottish lakes were contoured (unfortunately) from lake level downwards. As lake level may vary substantially it would have been far better to get into touch with land bench-marks.

Tithes.

The vexed question of tithes is one in which the plans are of singular importance. From 1837 onwards a number of tithe maps were made mainly at the scale of 3 chains to an inch (1/2376). There are about 12,000 of these tithe maps. They are remarkable for having cost the nation some £2,000,000 and of being (on the whole) unreliable. Their construction should have come after, and not before, the regular or accurate work of the Ordnance Survey. The original tithe maps were used for the commutation of tithes into tithe rent charges in cash.

Nowadays the question is not of commutation, but of redemption or altered apportionment, and both of these mean survey on the Ordnance plans.

The 6-inch.

The 6-inch is overshadowed in scale by the 25-inch, but it is just as important, and to many of us the more useful plan of the two.

It is universal in Great Britain, for the 15,000 sheets cover the whole to its remotest corner. There is only one matter in which it is not completely a " plan " and that is the widening of narrow streets in order to insert legible names. Areas cannot be stamped on it because single fields (or parcels) do not give enough room for them. Had the old parish books been kept up, however, the serial number might have appeared, and the combination would have been most useful. The addition of contours makes the 6-inch peculiarly valuable for matters of engineering or industrial development. The 6-inch is, par excellence, the country lover's plan. The footpaths are shown in great detail. I know of one man who keeps a series, extending for many miles round, on which all his walks are recorded. The local boundaries are generally of interest too, and the antiquities shown thereon give occasion for many a pleasant ramble.

A recent venture is the publication of the 6-inch in sheet lines convenient for each town directly revision has covered that part. These plans are on poor paper and reproduced with the minimum of labour in order to make it possible to publish cheaply. They are neither as reliable, nor as lasting, as the ordinary 6-inch, and show no contours. They cost, however, no more than a shilling.

Plans of Great Britain do not cover the Isle of Man, or the Channel Islands, except at the request and payment of the responsible authorities of these very charming islands. There are 6-inch plans of the Isle of Man and of Guernsey, however, and in Jersey an interesting experiment is resulting in good 12-inch plans. It so happened that there is a triangulation framework (see Chapter XVIII) available, and that a set of air photographs (none too good unfortunately) could be purchased. The opportunity for experiment was too good to loose. This is not the first time that a scale of twelve inches to the mile has been used, but it will be the only series of that scale in use at the moment.

Revision.

No survey, no plan, and no map, is of much value in a rapidly changing country unless it is periodically revised and republished. Before the Great War every plan was revised within twenty years of the date of its last publication. Then came economies which resulted in classing a largish part of the country as a forty-year revision area. But the staff kept diminishing and the building of houses and roads kept increasing until revision was wholly confined to small areas of great urgency. Naturally the greater the change since the last revision the greater the difficulty of fresh revision. Everything has, in fact, combined to interrupt reasonable revision just at the time when it is most needed for planning ahead. But perhaps the situation is on the mend. The revisers, who are constantly at work throughout Great Britain, are generally, though not always, serving soldiers. They have, with them, a warrant, which authorizes entry on private property. They are busy people with important documents on them, and naturally hope for the friendly treatment which they almost always get. On a hot summer's day a corporal and a sapper stood close together on the Great West Road looking at some documents concerning a name for the name book. They were suddenly parted by an overhasty cyclist. "Here," said the corporal, "what do you take us for? A guard of honour?" Such irritation has its excuses.

Conventional Signs.

There follows a selection or extract from the Conventional Sign Plate of the 25-inch. The more ordinary, and immediately understandable, signs are omitted, but all such odd abbreviations, and boundary symbols, as may become both important and difficult to follow, are included.

AN EXTRACT FROM THE CONVENTIONAL SIGN PLATE OF THE TWENTY-FIVE INCH

BOUNDARIES

Counties	▬ ▬ ▬
County and Civil Ph.	▬ · ▬ ·
Ridings	—+— —+— —+—
County Boroughs (England) ..	Co. Boro. Bdy.
County Burghs (Scotland) ..	Co. Burgh Bdy.
Municipal Wards	. Ward Bdy. ..
Urban Districts	_ U.D. Bdy. _ _
Police Burghs (Scotland)	_ Burgh Bdy. _ _
Rural Districts	ᵥ R.D. Bdy. ᵥ .
Civil Parishes	. . . . . .
Parliamentary County Divisions ..	Parly. Div. Bdy.
Poor Law Unions (Obsolescent) ..	. Union Bdy. . .
Parliamentary Boroughs	Parly. Boro. Bdy.
Divisions of Parly. Boroughs ..	Div. of Parly. Boro. Bdy
Municipal Boroughs	Munl. Boro. Bdy.

METHOD OF SHOWING THE BOUNDARIES IN CONNEXION WITH THE DETAIL

The initials are placed where a change occurs in the nature of the Boundaries, as referred to a road, wall, stream, drain, or fence, and the symbol ------ ⅟ ------ is used for marking the extent of the Boundary to which the initials refer.

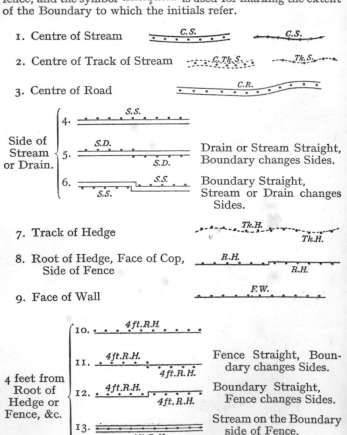

1. Centre of Stream   *C.S.*   *C.S.*

2. Centre of Track of Stream   *C.Tk.S.*   *Tk.S.*

3. Centre of Road   *C.R.*

Side of Stream or Drain.

4.   *S.S.*

5.   *S.D.*   *S.D.*   Drain or Stream Straight, Boundary changes Sides.

6.   *S.S.*   *S.S.*   Boundary Straight, Stream or Drain changes Sides.

7. Track of Hedge   *Tk.H.*   *Tk.H.*

8. Root of Hedge, Face of Cop, Side of Fence   *R.H.*   *R.H.*

9. Face of Wall   *F.W.*

4 feet from Root of Hedge or Fence, &c.

10.   *4ft.R.H.*

11.   *4ft.R.H.*   *4ft.R.H.*   Fence Straight, Boundary changes Sides.

12.   *4ft.R.H.*   *4ft.R.H.*   Boundary Straight, Fence changes Sides.

13.   *4ft.R.H.*   Stream on the Boundary side of Fence.

14.   *4ft.R.H.*   *4ft.R.H.*   Boundary Straight, Fence changes Sides.

15. Centre of Fence, Top of Cop,   *C.F.*   *T.C.*   *C.W.*
    Centre of Wall, &c.

16. Defaced or Undefined, Track of   *Def.*   *Tk.S.*   *Und.*
    Stream, Drain, or Fence

AREAS

Every parcel is numbered thus **27**

Its area is given underneath in Acres, thus   4·370

Braces, indicating
  that the spaces   The track in this case is excluded.
  so connected are
  included in the
  same reference   —,,——————,,———— included.
  number and area

ALTITUDES (in Feet)

The Altitudes are above the assumed mean level of the Sea
at Liverpool or Newlyn (as stated).   The Contour altitudes are
written thus...200.

Surface Levels along roads and to Trigonometrical Stations,
obtained by Spirit levelling, are written thus *326+*, the cross
showing the spot at which the altitude is taken.

Altitudes with the letters *B.M.* marked ↑ against them, refer
to marks made on Buildings, Walls, Milestones, &c. (Bench
Marks).

CONVENTIONAL SIGNS

Trigonometrical Station   ..   ..   △
Altitude at Trigonometrical Station   *507* △
Bench Mark   ..   ..   *B.M.325·9* ↑
Surface Level ..   ..   *342* +

Boundary Stone   ..   ..   ⎱   *B.S.*
——,,—— Post   ..   ..   ⎰ ° *B.P.*

Foot Bridge	..	..	..	.. *F.B.*
Foot Path	..	..	..	.. *F.P.*
Bridle Road	..	..	..	.. *B.R.*

High or Low Water Mark of Ordinary } *H.* or *L.W.M.O.T.*
    Tides ..   ..

High or Low Water Mark of Spring } *H.* or *L.W.M.S.T.*
    Tides ..   ..

Sluice	..	..	..	.. *Sl.*
Trough ..	..	..	..	.. *Tr.*
Spring ..	..	..	..	*Sp.*
Well	..	..	..	° *W.*
Mooring Ring ..	..	..		*M.R.*

Antiquities (Site of)	..	..	
Arrow denotes flow of water			

Electricity Pylon	..	..	..	▪ *E.P.*
Telephone Call Box	..	..	..	▪ *T.C.B.*
Police	—,,—	..	..	.. ▪ *P.C.B.*
Mile Stone	..	..	..	*M.S.*
Pump ..	..	..	..	*P.*
Signal Post	..	..	..	• *S.P.*
Guide Post or Board ..	..			*G.P.*
Letter Box	..	..	..	*L.B.*

Buying a Plan.

Those who want to buy plans had better look at Chapter XII on sheet lines, and either buy an index or consult the Ordnance Survey Agent. In most towns one of the principal booksellers or stationers acts as such. At agents you will find indexes, diagrams and catalogues. In London, Edward Stanford, Ltd., 12–14 Long Acre, W.C.2, or Sifton Praed & Co., Ltd., 67 St. James Street, S.W., are the agents. The former stocks all the plans; the latter the 6-inch only. A 25-inch costs 6s. 8d., and a 6-inch (quarter sheet), 2s.

Those who are interested enough to desire further information on the plans are recommended to read *The National Plans*—the 10-foot, 5-foot, 25-inch, and 6-inch scales—by Brigadier Winterbotham, H.M.S.O., 1934. 4s. 6d.

CHAPTER VI

Maps

A S stated in the introduction this book does not deal in the history of any maps which appeared before the start of an accurate national survey. On the other hand there is something of real interest in the way, and sequence, in which our present national maps grew, and even the earliest of them are still common enough in offices and libraries. A start must be made with the 1-inch because that was the first map to appear. The 10-mile, and later the ¼-inch, appeared primarily as indexes to the 1-inch, only reaching maturity and fulfilling their own proper purposes in recent times. The ordnance ½-inch is only 32 years old, for it did not begin until Bartholomew's ½-inch had shown what a useful scale this is. Lastly comes the 1/M, which has now passed from the national into the international sphere.

The 1-inch.

The first Director-General of the " Trigonometrical Survey ", as the Ordnance Survey was then called, was one of those people whose names one instinctively forgets. It was under General Mudge, the second Director-General, that the first sheet of the 1-inch appeared (in 1801). The start of an undertaking, new in character and technique, must take time, and there were grave difficulties in finding and training the field surveyors. The field work was to be done at two inches to the mile—a scale very different from the

3 or 4 chains to the inch characteristic of the work of
most private surveyors. It is, however, interesting to
notice some patches of field work on the 6-inch scale (as
in the Isle of Wight) and some 3-inch work in various
scattered spots.

The Corps of Royal Military Surveyors and Draughtsmen was formed in 1800, and had to be specially
trained in the field methods employed, which were a
mixture of ordinary chaining and of compass directions—just the same, in fact, as the methods General
Roy used in mapping the Highlands. The trigonometrical survey had, however, fixed the positions of
churches, and towers, and the tops of hills, and the
plotted field work, depending on and controlled by
these fixed positions, was a great advance on anything
previous.

Possibly Mudge's greatest difficulty lay in securing
enough good copper engravers. Copper printing was
the universal method of that day (and indeed, of most
of that century) for the printing of maps. The 2-inch
survey had to be reduced, by hand, to 1-inch as
a model, transferred to the copper, and then engraved thereon. Engraving was no new trade, but map-
engraving is a special branch of it, and every successive
sheet of this first map showed the improvement presently to culminate in the peculiarly beautiful work
of the " New Series ". Mudge's maps constitute the
" *old series* " or *first edition*. It is more than doubtful,
by the way, if anyone in those times thought of an
edition or sequence of editions. The habit of correcting
the copper plates as and when anything new had to
be shown, was entirely like the present time day to day
corrections to the copper plates of the charts. Thus,
amongst the copies still available of Mudge's first map
of Kent, published by W. Faden on the 1st January,
1801, it would be impossible to promise strict accord,
nor is it possible to say when this or that detail was
added. The first sheets of the " old series " were pro-

duced more or less as a county series. Kent—the first
—and Essex, which appeared in 1805, were made on
their own central meridians and were each divided into
four sheets for publication. Surrey and Sussex followed on their sheet lines. These four counties were
published in small bound folios containing the sheets
which cover the county, and indexed on the cover.
Thereafter procedure changed. The remainder of the
sheets of the old series were numbered, were all 23 inches
from north to south, but varied between 34 inches and
29 inches east and west. They were plotted on six
meridians, which were those of Dunnose, Clifton
Beacon, Burleigh Moor, Delamere, Moel Rhyddled, and
Greenwich. The original maps of Kent, Essex, Surrey
and Sussex, were brought into this number scheme, and
probably re-engraved after being " replanished " as
they called it in those days. In 1844 the old series
reached the Hull-Preston line and both methods and
execution were to suffer a drastic change.

Progress had been very slow, but the field staff employed on topography in England probably never ex-
ceeded 25 surveyors in the whole period. The start of
the Irish 6-inch in 1824 took the most of them away and
introduced the delays of training fresh hands.

Mudge's maps, or the " old series ", for most of them
appeared under his successor—General Colby—were of
course black and white. Lithography and colour
printing had not begun. There was, naturally, much
less to show then than there is now. Even so, however,
his map is heavy and none too legible. Hill features
were shown in hachuring[1] which, poor at the start,
rapidly improved, but they take charge of the map
too much. Woods are equally heavy, but the roads
are easy to follow. The lettering is perhaps the weakest
spot on them. Administrative boundaries did not
appear till long afterwards, and, what must have been
a serious drawback, footpaths and inns are not shown.

[1] See Plate II.

PLATE II

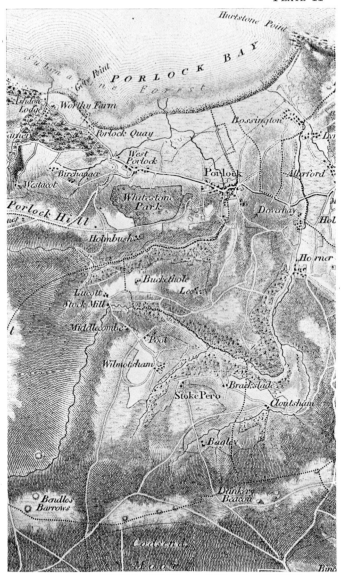

THE OLD SHEET SERIES: A BIT OF EXMOOR
Hachuring of 1820

The 1-inch was perhaps primarily a matter of national defence, for it began in the times of Napoleon, but it soon became known as "the hunting map". The other members of society of importance specially catered for were the archæologists, for early attention was given to mapping historical sites. There were no name books in this period. It is probably correct to add that the influence of Cassini's map of France was potent.

One more notable fact of these times was the advance in "hill sketching", or the drawing, on the ground, of the models on which the engravers based their hachures. This is dealt with in Chapter VIII.

The old series leaves a remarkable record behind, for the original 2-inch, 3-inch, and 6-inch surveys are an invaluable witness to contemporary facts of the countryside, and are often consulted for that purpose.

In 1840 the 1-inch entirely changed in character. The surveyors had just come back from Ireland, and the Government had resolved to survey the north of England and Scotland on the 6-inch scale. The 1-inch was to be a reduction from it. The "Battle of the scales" had begun. The 1-inch so reduced was for a time known as the cadastral 1-inch; a rather ridiculous misnomer; but, officially, it carried on the old series until it reached the border. There were important differences, however, between the southern and the northern blocks. One central meridian was chosen for the latter, that which passes through Delamere Forest (latitude 53° 13' 17·274″, longitude 2° 41' 03·562″), and the sheets, nominally 36 inches by 24 inches, were actually published in quarter sheets 18 inches by 12 inches. The larger scale survey had brought in name books, administrative boundaries and contours. It was at this time (1851–89) that parish boundaries were added to the southern sheets, but only in such cases as they appeared on the tithe maps—that is, only where the parish tithes had not previously been commuted into terms of cash.

The new sheets were numbered in succession to Mudge's maps as far as the border. The stage which cost most time was the preparation of hill sketches for the hachuring. In consequence of this delay an outline edition was issued without any hill features, and, when the hachuring was finished, new sheets were published.

The old series now complete (1870) but in halves of very different quality, it was decided to redo the older and southern half and to bring it into line with the portion reduced from the large scales. The northern sheets of this new edition were really exactly the same as before but were renumbered from the north. The southern sheets were finished in 1892, having England and Wales, at last, on one meridian. The final sheet number was 357, but actually there were only 354 sheets of this " *new series* " which, in fact, constituted the *second edition*.

Meanwhile, Scotland was to have the new idea in 1-inch mapping, as has happened again since. The French " Carte de l'état major ", at the scale of 1/80,000 had been brought out on the Bonne Projection (see Chapter IV), and it was thought wise to follow suit in Scotland, whereas England and Wales remained on the Cassini. The different projections for England and Scotland were a great nuisance for fifty years, and it was not until 1932 that all 1-inch maps of Great Britain formed a consecutive series. In other respects the 1-inch of Scotland exactly resembled the " new series ", or second edition of England and Wales, except that each of its 131 sheets was 18 × 24 inches in size.

An interesting point may be noticed here. In finishing off the " new series " it was found advisable to try photozincography. Now this means nothing more than using the camera to transfer the drawn map from its original paper on to a prepared zinc plate, and then printing from that. Public opinion was still strongly in favour of copper printing, which indeed gave far more beautiful results, but the engravers

were behindhand, as usual, and these zinc printed
maps were merely a stop-gap to serve till the real
article was ready.

Next comes the first inroad of colour printing.   It
was found that the frequent corrections to the detail
—the buildings, roads and railways—were injuring
the hachuring.   In other words the map might be
classed as partly permanent (the country) and partly
liable to change (the works of man).   It was decided to
separate these two, and it may be of interest to know
how you do separate one copper plate into two.   The
engraved printing plate held the ink in the lines and
letters and dots and symbols cut out of it by the
engraver.   This plate was placed in an electrolytic
(copper depositing) bath and fresh copper was deposited
on the engraved surface until it was thick enough to
remove as a matrix or " positive ".   Wherever the
engraver had cut a groove, the positive would have a
raised ridge.   From the positive it was easy to scrape
away such of these raised marks as were not required.
Then, in the electrolytic bath once more, a fresh
" negative " would be formed with only part of the
original map left on it.   In this way " hills " were
removed and put upon a separate plate, and then
printed in brown.   These black and brown 1-inch were
beautiful maps, and covered Great Britain by 1900.

In the important Committee of 1892 the need for
district maps had been pressed on the Government, and
criticisms, both unfriendly and misleading, were made
of the progress of national mapping, measured in terms
of Continental standards.   The fact was that no country
had embarked on anything like so comprehensive a
programme, or, indeed, needed it so badly, and the
staff was inadequate.   However, district sheets were
promptly put in hand, and at the same time the second
revision or *third edition* of the 1-inch began to appear.

The third edition took two forms.   The first was the
orthodox small sheet engraved and showing outline

and contours in black. These were all printed from copper and omitted the hachures of previous editions. 347 sheets went to England and Wales, whilst the revised Scottish sheets, in the same sheet lines and on the same Bonne projection as before, brought Scotland up to date. But the cry for coloured maps had put the main emphasis on the second and alternative form. The *large sheet series*, as it was called, assumed the duty of showing the hill features. The hachures were printed in a faintish brown, and contours were in red. Water was now shown in blue but the old habit of " water-lining " still obtained. Water-lining is a sort of under-water form-lining. It is attractive and can be made to show, rather well, how sharply or slowly the coast sinks to ocean levels. Generally the lines are closest together just below low-water mark and get further apart as one goes out to sea. From the point of view of economy in printing they are also advisable, since, for them, one requires just the sort of blue used for streams (and not the much lighter required for a general tint). Roads were in burnt sienna and woods in green. The 152 sheets of this series measured 27 × 18 inches each, and, for the first time in the history of official mapping, were mounted, folded, and given severely formal brown covers. In Scotland there was no need to enlarge the sheets for they had always been much larger than in England; but the same colour ideas were used to form an alternative edition, and, as in England, the engraved map was in outline with contours in black. The *fully coloured* series (as it was often called) was the first to be printed by lithography (which implies stone instead of zinc). Transfers were taken from the smaller copper plates and patched together on the stone. Litho stones are, however, a product peculiar to Bavaria, so that all this while advances in using the cheaper and handier zinc plate went on.

All corrections were still made on copper, however,

and transferred (on a piece of specially prepared transfer paper) from the copper plate to the stone. Six distinct and separate sets of stones, to equal the number of colours, and six times through the printing machine were now the rule. The black edition continued to be a necessity, because, for many legal and administrative measures, it is necessary to add colour washes to show up this or that matter of importance, and to add them to an already coloured map is to court disaster. The third edition was complete in 1912. The last 1-inch reviser had reached John o' Groats, crossed the water to the Orkneys and Shetlands, secured eventual approval for his work and moved his roving headquarters back to Land's End. The " Popular " or fourth edition was to begin, and the final doom of the " engraved " past was already in question. But at this prosperous time dreams of twenty colours per sheet were in the air. The French had made a real study of the " Marseilles " sheet—the first of the new 1/50,000 which was to supersede the old 1/80,000. We began to look to our laurels. There are, at the Ordnance Survey office in Southampton, some perfectly beautiful experiments of that time in colour printing. There is one of Somerset, for example, which would have been of the greatest value to King Alfred in his western battles with the Danes, for the features stand out so that no man can misunderstand. The best of them all was the " Killarney " sheet produced in thirteen printings and modelling the country perfectly. But the mountains, " lakes and isles " of that charming country lend themselves very readily to such treatment. Experiment must include Essex; and before minds were made up the Great War was upon us. Officers and men went to ply their indispensable calling in relatively unmapped lands (see Plate III) and the fourth edition was not born till 1919.

When the time came to get busy again on the national maps the financial situation was very different.

Economy was an urgent necessity, and it was decided firstly to retain the old copperplates, but to cut them up and rejoin them into new and more convenient sheet lines, and secondly to limit hill representation to contours only. Up to that time none but surveyed contours had been published. The popular edition was the first to " interpolate " and to show them at every fifty feet of altitude. The merits of these interpolated contours will be talked of in Chapter VIII.

The sheets of this edition are 27 × 18 inches, covering an area of 486 square miles each. The outline was, of course, in black, water required two different blues, woods in green, contours were in orange, and red and brown were kept for a rather ostentatious road classification. The day of road speed had begun. Seven colours and seven printings resulted in the clear and bold map which still covers most of Great Britain. A black or outline edition serves that disappearing class which still puts on colour washes for itself. During the early days of the " popular ", controversy continued on the losing fight engraving had to wage against more modern methods. The longest suit which engraving held was in the matter of record. A copperplate is relatively durable and lasting, although it loses shape and scale slowly under pressure.

Then it was decided to keep glass negatives as the record and to touch them up and correct them much as the portrait photographer removes the blemishes, and adds the missing, to the negative of his victim. The stronghold was taken, and the " popular " of Scotland was drawn, photographed, transferred to stone or zinc and printed, leaving the copperplate an honoured place in store. The main feature of the change is the much bolder and more legible series of alphabets adopted. Our fathers had a passion for " copperplate " writing. Its fineness and neatness was due to its medium and to the process of engraving. Boldness hardly goes with the engraver's tool.

PLATE III

MAPPING THE WESTERN FRONT

facing p. 76

Scotland profited, too, by the very nature of its features. The fifty-feet contours were in sufficient quantity, on its mountains and hills, to illustrate their subject properly, which is not the case in East Anglia. Finally an overlap of one inch, south and east, added convenience for the rambler. The size of sheet, 28×19 inches, is that of England and Wales with the overlap added, and ninety-one sheets carry the edition from the Mull of Galloway to Unst. For the first time England and Scotland appear on the same projection (the Cassini) and sheets across the border can be made up with a minimum of trouble. Two sheets are, in fact, common to both series.

The legal interval between revisions is fifteen years. Such a period varies greatly in significance according to the rate of development and reconstruction, and the years of the popular edition have been the busiest, in such matters, of our history. It has been necessary to make frequent partial revisions of roads, railways, reservoirs, afforestation schemes and such like matters. During the earlier years of the popular there was a natural reaction against the puritanical simplicity of the unsupported contour. Experiments in a fuller design were still carried on, therefore, and took the shape of the various " tourist " maps. These are, in fact, nothing else than the old district sheets in full dress. Many of them are very beautiful.

Once again the reviser has returned from the Shetlands to Land's End and the fourth revision is appearing on the fifth edition. Before starting on a drawing, to take the place of previous engraving, as had happened in the popular of Scotland, two important innovations were decided on. The map had to be fair drawn, willy nilly, because the old copperplates would not stand much more. Constant transfer from copper to stone or zinc is a matter costly in time, and in the struggle for perfect fit between contours and detail, detail and water. There was necessity, therefore, to make a " fair drawing ", and opportunity to get up to date in every conceivable way. The first decision concerned a minor change of projection. This is unimportant for the public but a convenience and a saving in survey. The change facilitates a new system of reference (see Chapter XI) and will, of course, presently involve Scotland as well as England. The other decision was a further change in the type of alphabet. The Scottish popular had taken the big stride, and now the fifth relief edition altered the shapes of letters, in the sense in which British typography was moving, going back more definitely to the style of the inscriptions on Trajan's Column. This style has critics. They may have some right on their side; but after all, the lettering on a map is not an end in itself. It is good in proportion as it is inconspicuously clear and legible, and if, at the same time, it is pleasant and well proportioned its highest value is attained. The new alphabets come very near to this desirable combination. All lettering on the 1-inch is by hand. There are so many names to go on an English sheet, so many things to fit in, that handwriting alone has the necessary elasticity. But it is also a curious fact that economically there is but little virtue, on a crowded sheet, in typing and stamping mechanically, or in photographic substitutes. The lettering must be individual to the case, and no matter of mass production.

The relief (or fifth) edition has two forms, as did the third; one gives a very good representation of the ups and downs, the surface modelling; and the other relies, for its hills, upon the unsupported contour. There is, as in Scotland, an overlap, but, in this case, north and east, of 2000 yards (a little more than an inch), and in the light of experience of the "popular" régime, the fifth edition once more shows those parish boundaries which the "popular" (of England and Wales) had omitted. Quite a row of new symbols come into action for the first time. There are National

Trust areas, youth hostels, wireless masts, electricity
transmission lines, and telephone call-boxes; but all
the old ones have still to be maintained, for the 1-inch
must continue to be the map for everybody. Critics
are vocal, invariably, on their own subject, but they
would be the first to object were that subject to suffer
for the convenience of the rest. Many of these critics
are little else than fast road travellers who love diagram-
matical simplicity and forget the needs of others. In
the new design of sheet lines (made necessary by the
new projection) the numbering of the sheets follows, as
closely as possible, that of the " popular ". There will
be the same number of sheets, it is understood, and
they are approximately the same size. In addition to
the normal edition, there are some fifty-seven district
and special sheets to cater for holiday areas, or those
of peculiar industrial importance.

The 10-mile (to 1 inch).

As the old series (Mudge's maps) began to cover
most of southern England, the need was felt for an
index to its meridians and sheet lines. The 1-inch
was reduced and engraved at 10 miles to the inch for
that purpose. But it was not only the Ordnance Survey
that required some really small scale general map.
" It is very useful . . . to show military and regimental
districts, headquarters of volunteers, post office districts, main telegraph lines, &c.," said a witness before
the 1892 committee. For sixty years or so (1840–1900)
an index it was, and, as it was reduced from the 1-inch
series of England and Scotland, the projections were
Cassini and Bonne respectively. In 1860 the Ordnance
Survey was asked to supply a river map for a Commission on Salmon Fisheries. The 10-mile index, with
rivers and catchment areas added from the 1-inch
became this " river map ". In 1867 a Royal Commission
on water supply used this same map, and in this year
the index was officially promoted to a place in the

estimates and to the status of a map. However, its
evolution continued to be uncommonly slow. The
reasons lay in the enormous amount of engraving to
be done on the 1-inch, and upon the effort begun in
1880 to finish off the 25-inch survey quickly. Presently
(in 1884) that portion which had been produced from
Mudge's compass and chain 1-inch was corrected to
agree with the " new series ", but even in 1892 it
was still more of an index than a map. Then at last
it was tackled seriously and in 1902 the original twelve
sheets of Great Britain were published. There were
two styles—one in outline (but water blue) and the
second with hill shading and sienna roads (in 8 sheets).
The hill shading, which is described in Chapter VIII,
was a sort of " stump " reduction of the general idea
of the hachures.

As almost everybody who uses maps wants a general
one of the whole as well as a larger one of a particular
part, the 10-mile became very popular. In 1924 it
was decided to redraw it, and the three sheets which
cover Great Britain were finished in 1926. The
result is a fully coloured and extremely useful map.
Heights are shown by contours at 200 and 400 feet
and thereafter at 400 feet intervals, and a very expressive " layer " system greatly helps to a quick grasp
of the country. It is easily the most useful general
map from which to get a broad idea. The layers contours and water (rivers, streams and sea) combined
make a very helpful physical map of Great Britain.
In 1933 there arose a need for an index to the Ministry
of Transport roads. A special edition was therefore
produced, in two sheets, with " A " class roads in red,
" B " class in purple, and A.A. and R.A.C. telephone
call boxes were also included. A general idea of hills
is given by using the old hill shading plates (in brown)
but, as the map was meant to be as clear and easy to
read as possible, no contours are given and not so many
names as on the fully coloured edition. Chapter XII

has something to say about its sheet lines and sizes. There is a useful " Civil Air Edition " of the 10-mile, which serves as a small air scale whilst the ¼-inch is the large one. This edition emphasizes the dangers and important guides of the normal landscape, and adds flying information and compass roses.

The ¼-inch.

The ¼-inch owes its start to the War Office and the Geological Survey. It was begun in 1859, and therefore inherited, as had the 10-mile, the somewhat doubtful outline of Mudge's maps. It was still being engraved in 1872, when every engraver had to be taken for the new 1-inch, and in 1884 an impatient reminder from the geologists, coupled with the assurance that a reduction from Mudge's maps in the south was quite good enough, led to its rapid conclusion. But the ¼-inch also suffered from the " index " inferiority complex, and was not published as a map until, in 1887, Mr. Stanford, the then head of the famous map firm, secured transfers for the benefit of sundry archæologists. This shook official complacency, and the ¼-inch " with its known imperfections " was published soon after. The original 25 sheets of England and Wales soon gave place to 18 and then to 10, the 17 of Scotland fell to 9, whilst they were still on the Cassini and Bonne projections of the respective 1-inch from which they were reduced. The two forms were (a) " engraved in outline " and (b) coloured blue for water, brown for hills, sienna for roads, and green for woods. The hills were shown by hill shading, and still, in the south, lurked the last traces of Mudge's maps. Then in 1912 the preparation of a new ¼-inch was begun. The engravers just had time to finish off the sheet of Kent (the first to appear) when the Great War put a temporary stop to it. In 1918 it was re-started, but all the rest of the map was drawn for the camera, and this scale escaped from the engraver.

There were 21 sheets of this series to cover Great Britain (now all in one projection) but the last had appeared before the full significance of the car and the Ministry of Transport had been realized, for this, *par excellence*, is the map for the owner-driver. In 1928 sheet lines were changed again in an A series, which went some way to meet public convenience. Ministry of Transport numbers were added to the roads, and the result, clear and legible, excellent in its presentation of physical features, lacked but three things to secure its greatest value for motoring. These were, better traffic directions in the margin, still further changes in sheet lines, and a fold and cover specially designed for motoring comfort. A later edition still is just appearing with these three additions. For the sake of clarity the old tree symbols have gone and a simple green shows the woods. It seems a pity, but still the ¼-inch is not of much value in forestry analysis anyhow. A very useful addition are the traffic sketches of towns, which appear within the cover.

For a rambler the ¼-inch would seem a very small scale, but for airmen it is on the large side. A special "Civil Air Edition" picks out those features of the normal editions most useful to airmen. Railways, main roads, woods, inland water, and high ground are emphasized, and such affairs of characteristic appearance from the air as race courses and golf courses have been clearly marked. On top is overprinted a special air information plate, to show aerodromes, landing grounds, mooring areas (seaplane), wireless stations, prohibited flying areas, danger areas, air customs, and the like.

The ½-inch.

The Boer War had, as everyone knows, a chastening and sharpening effect on the British Army. We learnt to earmark the largest ant heap in sight for our next step forward, to regard every fold in the ground

with deep suspicion, and to look on a good map as at
once unexpected and heaven sent. In the period which
followed that war the officer studied ground and maps
as never before nor since. Now Bartholomew had
just produced a very excellent ½-inch, based upon the
Ordnance 1-inch. It offered an attractive layer system,
and a wider opportunity for the strategically minded
and brass-hatted, than the 1-inch. He bought, but
grumbled, and so it was that the Ordnance Survey
was charged with making a national ½-inch. When,
after a period of protracted interchange of minutes,
we come to a national decision, then haste is the order
of the day, and so it was with the ½-inch. There was
no time to "write" names, nor was there an adequate
supply of sufficiently trained draughtsmen, but typers
and stampers existed. The map was drawn and was,
indeed, the first to escape altogether from copper.
Forty sheets for England and Wales and 34 for
Scotland completed the programme. The sheets are
27 × 18 inches and there are two editions, the hill-
shaded and the layered. Contours are in brown, water
blue, roads sienna, and woods green. The result is a
very good map. The names are a trifle small for the
scale and the detail (occasionally revised for roads and
railways) wants redrawing to record the growth of
building during the last busy years. As do all Ordnance
maps, the ½-inch gives a guaranteed accuracy (at the
date of publication) and a wealth of detail, but it
may be regarded (in its present form) as alternative
to Bartholomew's, and the choice lies principally in the
convenience of the respective sheet lines. In the early
days of its appearance there was an edition which
included contours, hill shading and layers. Some of
the south-easterly sheets in this style—those, for
example, of the Chilterns and North and South Downs
—are most expressive. Unfortunately the "layer"
scheme used itself up, too soon, in the browns and
got into pink and purple trouble for high altitudes.

When combined with a hill shading, in such sheets as that of Alnwick, the result is too formidable to be either pleasant or instructive.

There are some who prefer the ½-inch to any other small scale. They may reasonably say that the ½-inch has been allowed to suffer too much from the economy of the times. There are, however, at least three quite beautiful ½-inch special sheets. The Isle of Skye in some seven printings equals the beauty of the Killarney 1-inch and gives the whole island on one sheet. The Cotswolds (with Oxford in the south-east corner) covers that attractive region. The London traffic area is a new drawing in the style of the relief edition of the 1-inch. It is a very large map, 24 × 35½ inches. It is on the new projection, with the new system of reference, and the value to Londoners of so detailed a single sheet stretching from Royston to Horsham, must be quite exceptional.

The 1/M (or 1/1,000,000—15·782 miles to the inch).

It is proper, at this present time, to end off a chapter on national achievement by passing to the international. During the last quarter of the nineteenth century geographers had been groping after some universal map with standardized conventions. Obviously the scale would have to be small or the series would never get far in a largely unsurveyed world. There was beginning to be talk of the scale of 1/M, as convenient, not too small to show the important, nor too large to be feasible. It was largely due to this new feeling that the Ordnance Survey engraved a map of Great Britain on the scale of 1/M, starting in 1908 and publishing the two sheets in 1913. These are beautifully engraved maps with a brown hill shading and water in blue. The southern sheet extends to Alnwick, and the northern to the Shetlands. The projection is a rectified conical with two standard parallels.

It was actually during the preparation of this map

that international agreement on conventions was
secured, and that certain nations agreed to contribute
small yearly sums to a central office (the Ordnance
Survey was chosen), and to share the responsibility by
sheets rather than by national territories. Unfortunately, sheet lines, difficult enough to arrange well for
one small country, cannot but be awkward for a world-
wide series. As the Greenwich meridian is one of the
sheet lines and the sheet line parallels fall awkwardly
in Great Britain, no less than seven of these international
1/M maps have to be procured before the country is
complete. For that reason two special sheets on the
international style have now been produced for British
needs, and the previous 1/M has been allowed to lapse.
The international value of this series is great, and a
special chapter (Chap. XIII) is devoted to it.

Maps of Ireland.

A special word should be said about the maps of
Ireland. The 1-inch, 10-mile, ¼-inch and ½-inch of
Ireland grew with, and in the same fashion as, those
of Great Britain. In 1921 the Home Rule Act severed
the survey of the Irish Free State from the Ordnance
Survey, and at the same time Northern Ireland undertook her own survey operations. The offices at Belfast
and Dublin are therefore the headquarters of independent surveys with policy and progress to remould in
accordance with their own problems.

Ireland, like Scotland, had adopted a Bonne Projection for her small-scale maps. The sheets of the
1-inch were however only 18 inches by 12 inches like
those of the English small sheet series. There were
205 of these sheets, and they were produced in five
printings, black, blue, brown for hills, sienna for roads,
and green for woods. Then there were the usual combined and district sheets numbering 42.

The 10-mile was a single sheet, $36 \times 26\frac{1}{2}$ inches, in
outline, or in three colours. The ¼-inch had 16 sheets

(18 × 12 inches) either in outline or in four colours. The ½-inch had 25 sheets of larger size (27 × 18 inches) and with a good many overlaps. This was an excellent contoured series, but a layered edition (additional to the ordinary) never quite covered the country, missing out most of the east and south.

No doubt most, if not all, of these maps are still purchasable.

General.

Practically any large bookseller or stationer will provide all the sorts of maps mentioned in this chapter. Naturally prices vary a little. Some of the larger sheets cost more than others. An average figure may be taken as: Paper flat, 1s. 6d. to 1s. 9d.; paper folded in covers, 1s. 9d. to 2s.; mounted on linen, folded in covers, 2s. 6d. to 2s. 9d.; section mounted and folded in covers, 4s. to 4s. 3d. Thus covers add 3d., linen mounting adds 9d., and section mounting 2s. 3d.

Those who are interested in the maps of Great Britain will find a mine of information in:

1. *The Published Maps in the Atlases of Great Britain and Ireland*, 1579–1870, by Thomas Chubb (Homeland Association, Ltd.). £2, 2s.

2. *Maps, their History and Uses*, by Sir George Fordham (Cambridge University Press, 1921). 7s. 6d.

3. *The Map of England*, by Colonel Sir Charles Close (Peter Davies, 1932), 6s., which deals with the various attributes of the national 1-inch.

4. *Maps and Survey*, by Arthur R. Hinks (University Press, Cambridge, 1933), 3rd Edition. 12s. 6d. This deals with cartography generally, including a brief history of early maps, and an analysis of contemporary foreign maps.

CHAPTER VII

Charts

THE earliest property map was made long before the first geographical map or first chart. The two latter were at first more or less the same thing, however, for they did not diverge into their present distinctive forms until voyages had spread from the coastal waters of the Mediterranean to the oceans. There is neither room nor excuse in this chapter for embarking on history which antedates the official labours of the Hydrographic Department. That has been done exhaustively elsewhere. The two main factors in the evolution of hydrography have been the mariners' compass and the introduction of Mercator's Projection. The first gave to sailors the freedom of the seas, and the second, superseding the plane surveys of the Mediterranean, made it possible to chart the globe.

Dutch, French, and Spanish seamen were ahead of us in hydrography, and the first official labours of the Department of Hydrography were the copying of these foreign charts. We can begin, then, at 1750, when these copyings were in hand and when Lawrie, Purdie, and Arrowsmith were publishing charts of unofficial origin. It was then that Mr. Murdoch MacKenzie made, for the Admiralty, charts of the Orkneys and Shetlands, and of the northern and western coasts of Scotland and Ireland. These were based on compass bearings and a rough compass triangulation, just as was the contemporary map of the Highlands made by General Roy.

In these early days there was no Hydrographer, but a Head Maritime (or Nautical) Surveyor, and sailors took to charting as part of their normal duties without, necessarily, having specialized in the subject.

That remarkable man Captain James Cook was to the Hydrographic Department what Roy was to the Survey. In 1768 he was sent to the South Seas there to observe a transit of Venus. The Royal Society fathered the project and astronomy comes as naturally from the sailor (the Astronomers Royal even to-day serve their Lordships of the Admiralty) as does geodesy from the soldier. Curiously enough the church may be said to take second place in both. It was on this voyage that Cook discovered the eastern shores of Australia, and it was his practice to chart, with uncommon skill, where he explored. His principal fields lay in the Pacific and on both the eastern and western coasts of North America. In these early days there was much scientific research and measurement of all sorts upon the oceans. Hydrographers and explorers took ocean temperatures, samples of marine life, and by 1770 or so were sounding down to 800 fathoms (a fathom is six feet). It was at this time (1773) that the first " station pointer " was evolved. In surveying coastal waters position is found by observing the angles subtended at the boat by three known points ashore. The three movable limbs of the station plotter are set, against a scale, to the measured angular distances, and the centre point (when the arms fit against the known positions on the chart) solves the resection problem automatically (see Chapter X). It was in the year before that Kendall's chronometer, made from Harrison's design, earned for the latter the very handsome reward of £10,000 from Parliament. This chronometer was employed by Cook on the second of his famous voyages.

Broadly speaking, navigation rested on compass bearings from charted positions; and those positions (in deep-sea sailing) were found by sextant and chronometer (amplified by logged distances, compass directions, and times—a method known generally as " Dead Reckoning "). The sextant is just an instrument which measures the angle between two points (for example, the altitude of the sun above the horizon). With its help both latitude and local time could be measured, whilst the chronometer, recording Greenwich time with fair precision, and therefore the difference between local and Greenwich times, gave the longitude.

Sir John Franklin, who gave his life in that prolonged quest for the North-West Passage, was another early hydrographic surveyor.

Coming to the real beginnings of the present Hydrographic Department, dating officially from 1795 and therefore almost a twin of the Ordnance Survey, we find Alexander Dalrymple as the first Hydrographer. A well-known successor of his, Rear-Admiral Beaufort, K.C.B., D.Sc., F.R.S., occupied the post of Hydrographer from 1829 to 1855. He was the contemporary of General Colby of the Ordnance Survey and it is curious that two such brilliant men should have been in survey office at one and the same time. Perhaps his most lasting memorial are the arrows and abbreviations of the weather map of to-day (see Chapter XV). Captain FitzRoy was another hydrographic expert, though never actually Hydrographer, and it was with him that Charles Darwin, the famous scientist, took ship (in the *Beagle*) on hydrographic work round South America. During this voyage the Spanish charts of those waters were found on occasion to be twenty-five miles in error. From that day to this a succession of brilliant officers, often members of the Royal Society, and as often ending their careers as Colonial Governors, have devoted themselves to hydrographic surveying. It is time to discuss some of their doings.

But, to start with, what is it that they must survey? The answer is every peril of rock, shoal and coast which threatens navigation, and every fact provided by nature or man which may help in avoiding them. The facts of greatest consequence are the depths of underwater dangers and the positions of navigation marks and prominent features. Soundings read generally from Mean Low-water Springs, but each chart should be consulted specially. The datum is, sometimes, a little lower than this. Soundings are normally in fathoms, but in shoal waters are often given in fathoms and feet, the latter appearing in smaller figures behind and below as for example,

$$5_2 \quad 7_4 \quad 9_3.$$

Exposed banks and shoals are amplified by spot heights in feet above the same chart datum and underlined as,

$$\underline{4} \quad \underline{7} \quad \underline{1},$$

whereas all other heights on dry land are in feet above Mean High Water Springs. Modern charts are contoured on the land surface, a practice of fairly modern times. Charts of earlier date are all hachured (see Chapter VIII). "Fathom lines" or sea-bed contours are, of course, referred to the datums of soundings. The most prominent are those which give the six-fathom and ten-fathom lines. These correspond to the notice "You have been warned" on a highway under repair, and are directed at ships of normal and heavy draught respectively. As mentioned in Chapter V, the datum for Ordnance Survey tidal lines is mean level ordinary tides, and contours are from Mean Sea Level. Although there is no gap between the land and sea surveys there is a difference of datum. Temporary dangers such as wrecks are considered safe 8 fathoms (48 feet) below the chart datum, but the hydrographer's duty includes the charting of all ocean depths, and he may find himself sounding in 5000 fathoms as well as in eight.

Coastwise sailing is governed to a great extent by

conspicuous points ashore. The hydrographer must therefore show just as much of that shore as is useful to his purpose. If there is a reliable land survey he will use it. "Topography is taken mainly from the Ordnance Survey" is the usual remark to find on charts of home waters, but the actual coastline is generally put in by hydrographic surveyors as a matter of training. In Great Britain the 6-inch is therefore of much assistance to chart making and there are also lists of the positions of all those stations of the Grand Triangulation which govern the land survey. (The first use of the Ordnance Survey Triangulation for hydrography dates back to the beginning of last century.) Elsewhere in the world the hydrographer may have to complete the whole of the land survey for himself, and may have to begin by finding the latitude and longitude of his first and guiding point.

The land surveyor has to start from a measured line (or "base"). The hydrographer may have to do the same, and if so uses a steel tape or chain if he can measure on shore; if not he runs out a wire from a drum astern. A weight at the end drops to the bottom and the wire, running from point to point on the sea-bed, measures lengths of two or three miles with an error of, say, a foot in a mile. The buoys which mark the ends of this base are the equivalent of the surveyor's beacons. Ashore the hydrographer uses the best of the land surveyor's tools; afloat, he uses the sextant; for he can hold that steady enough on a deck on which land instruments would be impossible. Soundings were, in the old days, measured by dropping a weight till it hit the bottom, and then measuring the depth in fathoms, as shown on the attached line (or wire). Everyone has heard of "heaving the lead". Nowadays they are measured, as often as not, with an echo sounder. An electrical impulse from the ship sends the sound down to hit the sea-bed, from which it is reflected (or echoed) upwards again to a recording machine. The speed at which sound travels in water is the underlying factor. Then each point at which a sounding has been taken is surveyed and plotted on the chart. In coastal waters the survey depends on known positions ashore. Out of sight of land the surveyor must fix his latitude and longitude. To-day the hydrographer and the navigator are independent of the chronometer, for they can get Greenwich time on the wireless. Everyone familiar with charts will remember how soundings often run in lines this way or that (often like a W). This is, of course, due to sounding along straight lines between fixed positions. It seems strange that even to-day some hundreds of newly found rocks may be charted in a year, until one remembers that some sixty or seventy per cent of the land surface is not yet surveyed in any precise sense; and the land surface is so much easier because it can be seen. The Hydrographic Department has about eight ships constantly at work of which four are in home waters; and the year's work includes the field or sea surveying and thereafter a spell of plotting in the chartroom. A great life it must be.

During the plotting period many soundings may be omitted. All of them help in drawing fathom lines (or sea-bed contours) but not all may be necessary if there is a general similarity of depth. The greatest number of soundings allowed is something less than 200 in the square inch.

Naturally hydrographic surveying depends a good deal upon international co-operation. There is honour among thieves—and professional brethren—and so it is amongst the land and sea surveyors of the world. The Marine Survey of India, like the Survey of India, has a long and distinguished record. The Dominions now have their own hydrographic services; Canada has surveying ships, a hydrographic office, and publishes her own charts. Australia has now a surveying ship and an office at Sydney, and there is an Inter-

PLATE IV

PLOTTING A BEACON

facing p. 92

national Hydrographic Office agreeably placed at Monaco. Similar international effort will be noted in Chapter XV on " the weather map ".

In Chapter IV on projections the distaste of a land surveyor for Mercator's projection is made evident. It is a real nuisance to have maps which distort the world so badly as do those on Mercator, but the sailor has to depend largely upon what he calls the " rhumb " line (pronounced, suitably enough, as " rum "). The Mercator makes a compass bearing (a loxodrome or rhumb line) into a straight line, and plots it correct in angle however long it may be. Obviously so important a matter as to make the Mercator a necessity for him. All small-scale charts of general nature are plotted on it except those of polar regions which are on the gnomonic (as are, often enough, large-scale charts of harbours). Otherwise, of course, a Mercator of the poles, having reached infinity in a mathematical sense, would place still further impediments in the way of polar exploration.

Charts have no particular editions. Quite minor corrections are inserted on all available copies by hand, and all corrections are inserted on the copper plate. In this latter particular they are just like Mudge's first 1-inch. The copper plate is " replanished " (knocked up from behind), corrected, strengthened maybe by a copper deposit, and used for a reprint. The number printed is that for current use, and the dangers of the sea are never allowed to accumulate unpublished. Agents correct by hand from the *Notices to Mariners*. Something of this sort is gradually evolving also for the use of Airmen. Obviously the safety of navigation either at sea or in the air demands such special measures and makes the periodical, and often long delayed, revisions characteristic of maps and plans impossible. For these reasons copper is still the standby of the Hydrographic Department, some of whose plates are already well over a century old. Nowadays, however, printing is generally done by taking a " transfer " from copper and laying it on a zinc plate (Chapter XIX will explain). The Mercator itself makes any consecutive and continuous series of a fixed size of sheet an impossibility. The scale varies too greatly. Charts are made to suit the necessities of each individual case. The Admiralty has some 4000 in all, of which 400 refer to Home Waters. A special extract from the chart catalogue lists these home-water charts for the benefit of yachtsmen. Some idea of the activity of the Hydrographic Department may be got from the fact that over half a million charts are printed every year, that 2000 *Notices to Mariners* are issued, and that a hundred or so of entirely new charts appear.

Agents and Prices.

The Admiralty agents for charts are Messrs. J. D. Potter of 145 Minories, London, E.C.3, and sub-agents are found in most ports. A list of these sub-agents is given at the end of each volume of *Sailing Directions*, *Light Lists*, and in the catalogue. The price of each chart is to be found just under the Hydrographic Office seal (always printed on the chart).

Literature.

1. *Catalogue of Admiralty Charts and other Hydrographic Publications*, H.M.S.O., 1934–35.
2. Extract from the above for Home Waters.
3. *How the British Admiralty Charts are Produced*, by Gerald R. Hayes (reprinted from an article in the *Nautical Magazine*, 1927).
4. *On the Correction and Use of Charts*, published by J. D. Potter (the Admiralty agents), 1931.
All these, with the exception of the catalogue, are agreeably marked " Gratis ".
5. *Charts: Their Use and Meaning*, by A. Herbert Fowler, published by J. D. Potter, 1931. 6s. 6d.

Marine Measures of Length.

A nautical or sea mile is the length of a minute of latitude. As this varies from place to place (the earth is not quite spherical) a mean value is used. The Admiralty value in feet is taken as 6082·4.

1 sea mile = 10 cables (each therefore actually about 608 feet, but for ordinary purposes taken to be 600 feet).

1 cable = 100 fathoms (each 6 feet).

A knot is a measure of speed, not of distance. Thus 20 knots means a speed of 20 sea miles an hour.

CHAPTER VIII

Hills

The eye of knowledge is as a telescope to the common eye, by which more is apprehended than is immediately seen.—*Ruskin*.

HILLS are of the greatest interest and importance to all of us; yet they are by far the most difficult features for the map to show. Somehow or other they must be made to stick up from the flat sheet of paper, at all the different gradients, and with all the minor features, which characterize them. By far the most widely used method is that of contouring, for which reason a brief explanation of it was included under Map Conventions. But in this chapter we may with profit go back to the beginning.

In 1854 the " delineation of hill features " was much discussed. One of the many committees on the Ordnance Survey was in session. The Treasury and the Ordnance Survey had voluminous correspondence with all sorts of notable people, and fortunately all these letters have been preserved. It will be convenient to follow out ideas, for a while, and to quote at random.

One witness starts our subject by saying: " Give me a faithful picture of rivers, streams and lakes, and I will fill in the mountains for myself ". This gentleman, something of an optimist, expressed too vigorously a great truth. If there is any difficulty in following contours or hill shading look at once for the streams. A favourite question on map reading is to give a selection of unnumbered contours with no streams shown, and to ask the victim to separate spur from valley. Fortunately such a problem never occurs in map-

reading with a reasonable map. There are bound to
be water courses, even if they are dry very often, and
these are bound to show the question of drainage.
Moreover they are also bound to show the best graded
lines. If contours are accurate you will find that they
tend to space out evenly along a stream. They must
do so, in fact, if there are neither waterfalls nor rapids.
Naturally in the higher reaches and up towards the
source the slope will get steeper and contour intervals
will narrow, but for all that the stream is the best
graded line of nature. There is, therefore, very little
trouble on an ordinary map in saying which is valley
and which is spur. Where there is a lake there must
be a basin to hold the water. But the problem of hill
delineation, made easier by the water, is not thereby
solved. It may be a question of Ben Nevis, of Largo
Law, of the Scarp of the Cotswolds, or of Dartmoor.

In Saxton's times, and even in those of Napoleon,
hills were often shown in profile, as now we show a
lighthouse. We can dismiss that method, at once, as
of no value to-day, for the consequences to the topography of Bangor or Fort William if we upset Snowdon
or Ben Nevis northwards, are too ridiculous to contem-
plate. Then, in such histories as that of Napier's
Peninsular War, hills and mountains are shown as long
hairy caterpillars. This method is the purest convention. It can give no idea of real shape except in
the case of small isolated hills. The caterpillar method,
with its small penstrokes down the slopes, however,
leads to hachuring, and as hachures still appear on
many maps, although generally in modified form, the
method must be discussed.

Hachures and contours are, by definition, at right
angles to each other. The hachure is drawn vertically
down the slope. An early example of hachuring on
our official maps is that of Mudge's map of Somerset (see
Plate II). For its time it was good, but it had evolved
very little from the hairy caterpillar stage. Anyone who

knows Porlock will recognize certain features and miss others. No one who did not know it would be very much the wiser for the map; whilst the amount of printer's ink used is out of proportion to its usefulness. But hachuring very rapidly improved. The long strokes of Mudge's first attempt were made much smaller. Hachuring finally became a lot of consecutive bands of short penstrokes, all broken, all vertical to the slope, closer and darker on the steeper slopes, opener and finer on the flatter. A regular table or guide gave the depth of stroke and the distance between them in terms of the gradient. The small sheet series[1] is an admirably hachured map. It became a matter of routine to lighten the hachuring on the lower slopes and darken above so as to emphasize height and not to interfere with the lower levels where ground is valuable and the map has so much to record.

For a moment one had best break off to emphasize that side point. Whatever method is adopted should leave the valleys free of colour or dark lines, if that is possible. It is just there that hill features are of the least significance and where the detail of the map is thickest.

To return to hachures we may say that they fail to give any accurate idea of height. Take a large high plateau such as Dartmoor for example. Hachures will show the minor features on Dartmoor, but give no indication whatever of their height above mean sea level. On the other hand they pick out small features, which contours may miss, and give a valuable picture of breaks of slope or minor differences of direction of slope.

This peculiarity of hachuring, that it explains in detail even if it does not measure, is responsible for opinions in its favour which have been common from mountaineering clubs. Going back to the original correspondence of 1854, let me quote Sir Roderick Murchison, President of the Royal Geographical Society at that time: "I beg to express my most

[1] A term often applied to the quarter sheets of the "Old" and "New" Series.

decided conviction that they produce nothing on the Continent equal to our best maps" (hachured old series), "of which I lay what I consider a beautiful example before the Committee . . . If I add to that . . . the height of every principal mountain, hill and valley, then I have everything that, as a geographer or geologist, I can desire . . ." So, although an advocate of hachures, he did desire something definite, as well as something descriptive.

One often wonders why the original hachure experts chose to draw them vertically down the slope instead of horizontally, as if they were portions of contours, or form lines. Several good maps of the Continent were made on that horizontal hachure principle. It is just as flexible and tends to give that step effect which helps appreciation of height. Indeed, the Ordnance Survey "hill sketchers", who worked on the ground in order to produce the model for the "hill draughtsmen", always drew their sketches in this way. These old hill sketches, generally at six inches to the mile, are still used in all sorts of ways.

As a method, hachuring has this grave disadvantage, that it calls for very special training both in the field and in the office. It is relatively expensive and, probably, will never be undertaken again for any extended area. But it remains, once done and well done, at the service of the public.

Hachures were engraved for the 1-inch. In 1850 or so came the problem of providing a similar illustration of hill features for the ¼-inch. The method chosen was that known as hill shading. In theory this shading was supposed to be such as would result from light falling vertically on a model of the ground. The slopes would then be in shadow, in proportion to the steepness of their gradients. In practice, hill shading was a copy, drawn on stone or zinc, of the general effect of the hachures. This sort of hill shading found its way successively on to the ¼-inch, 10-mile, ½-inch, and 1/M.

It is not very expressive and is very generalized, but is sometimes useful in conjunction with other methods.

Whilst Mr. Dawson, our most famous hill sketcher, was actually busy on Snowdon, General Colby "fell upon" the method of contouring during his work on the Irish 6-inch. It was an immediate success and was discussed at length in the correspondence I have mentioned above. "What do you consider the best method? . . ." Colonel Yolland was asked. "By contours . . . There is not the slightest doubt upon the subject; it does not admit of a question at all that the contours are perfectly accurate, whilst this, on the contrary (shading by vertical hachures) gives no information beyond the pictorial effect." But again from the Board of Health: "I perfectly agree . . . that it would be quite impossible to bring out a correct representation of the shape from the mathematical contours alone." ("Perfectly" was evidently a fashionable word at this time.) By contouring was, however, understood, in those days, the accurate tracing of such lines by level along the countryside, and then the accurate survey of the pegs on to the map. Broadly speaking the contours thus surveyed were the 50, 100, and by hundreds to 1000, 1250 and by two-fifties to the top (though there are many exceptions and alternatives in different counties). The verdict which actually carried that day was voiced by Major Larcom. "I entirely feel the desirability, in point of economy, of reducing hills to a mere mechanism, which the presentation of ground by contours alone would completely effect, but I think it would produce but an imperfect representation of the country and the public have a right to expect that the national map shall be a triumph of art as well as of science."

As a consequence we find the small sheet series with hachures in brown and with contours.

Now to consider contours. Nowadays, in the world at large, they are generally far below the standard of the surveyed contours of our own national series. There are countries, I will not particularize, which acquire a somewhat inadequate number of levels in the field and leave to draughtsmen who have never been on the ground the task of drawing contours to fit. Such contours as these are worse than hill shading which is based on ground sketching. They become, in fact, just a poor method of hill shading, all the more misleading in that they assume a scientific form and disguise their office origin. The usual style of contouring is, however, intermediate in kind between the fully surveyed and the sketched. Generally it depends upon individual measured heights and is put in by eye on the ground. It can be, and generally is, very helpful, and particularly so as it is easy, on the ground, to amplify the number and decrease the interval. Contours must however be constant in interval all over the area of the map. Our first contoured maps were most misleading where they changed from an interval of 100 feet to one of 250 feet (at the 1000-feet line). On the one hand it would be most helpful in East Anglia to put, on the 1-inch, contours at a vertical interval of 25 feet, but, on the other, if these were included on a 10-mile of Great Britain which elsewhere stuck to its much larger interval the result would be dreadful. On the last two (4th and 5th) editions of the 1-inch, contours at 50 feet interval are interpolated on the old hill sketches. The surveyed contours are plotted on hill sketches, and the shape given by the latter makes it easy to interpolate fairly well. It is as well to realize, however, that they have just the local accuracy of the sketches and no more. They help to give the mental picture which is so important.

The rambler, or holidaymaker generally, is not so particular about the exact height. He wants to see the country on the map without having to search and analyse. In Scotland, Wales, or the Lakes, there are contours enough to show up things. It is just in the most developed places, and in East Anglia in particular, where the contour does least for one. A small feature of 40 feet high may have been important from prehistoric times down to to-day and peculiarly noticeable in its flat surroundings. Yet it may entirely escape an unsupported 50-feet contouring.

It is to the firm of Bartholomew that we owe the first good layered series of topographical maps of this country, and most popular has this system become. It consists of showing all the ground, between two contours, in its own distinctive tint or colour layer. These layer tints get darker and darker as the altitude increases. Generally they begin on a green layer from mean sea level to 50, or 100, or 500 feet according to the range of height which has to be covered. The idea of the green is, no doubt, the colour of lush low-lying valley meadows. It is most misleading where it is applied to the many dry and dusty shore levels of lands where the rains break far up on the hills and never reach the dry coast.

On such high plateaus as those of South Africa, the layer tint, dark because of the altitude, may extend unbroken and unhelpful over thousands of square miles. It was a matter of the greatest difficulty to evolve a system of layer tints for the International million map, because a sheet of the Sahara and another of the Himalayas include contrasts, and imply a range of tint, so great that neither can be really successful. Contours may be multiplied without much difficulty, but tints are confined to what the printing machine can do in a reasonable number of printings.

For these reasons there are seldom as many layers as contours, and the effect is to split the height to be shown into bigger steps and to lose the minor shapes. For all that layering is the only system which separates at a glance plateau from the lower plain. It provides a sort of guide to the contouring. It is peculiarly helpful to those many who understand what contours

are, but cannot turn them into a helpful picture of
the ground. The War Office 1/4M of Asia and 1/2M
of Africa are beautifully layered. The layer printings
of the 10-mile are a splendid physical picture of Great
Britain. But a good layer scheme must avoid violent
transitions of colour, which spoil that very mental
picture it is meant to convey.

Finally we come to shadow. Shadow is supposed to
be thrown on the map by a light to the north-west
(see p. 27). It throws up slopes, therefore, which fall
to the south-east, and so is of no help in picking out
such important features as the scarps of the Cotswolds
and Chilterns, which face north-west and get no shadow.
By itself it is a very poor method of showing hill
features. The French 1/100,000 Carte vicinal, which
relies upon it, is a poor map in consequence. It has a
certain value, however, in helping to throw up hills to
the eye where it is used to supplement other methods.

To recapitulate:

Hill delineation must provide

(a) An accurate guide to height.
(b) A correct representation of local features.
(c) A quick mental picture.

Now no nation has the ideal survey, but most have
acquired, in the course of time, a number of different,
and partial, pictures of the ground. These are:

(1) Contours at stated intervals. These provide for
(a), are rather weak on (b) and fulfil (c) only where the
hills are steep and bold.

(2) Measured heights of hills, passes, valley bottoms,
and so on. These are a help to (a).

(3) Hachures (probably antedating the contours) or
hill shading. Printed lightly, these help (b) and greatly
facilitate (c).

(4) Hill shadows. A help to (c).

(5) The data for layering inherent in (1). Layers are
a help to (c).

In a really modern survey of mountainous countries, such as that now being done in Switzerland, contours can be surveyed at small intervals and in great number from photographic material. These provide for all requirements. But one must remember that nothing less than contouring at a 10-foot interval would give a quick mental picture of East Anglia.

Most European national maps therefore use (1), (2), (3) and (4), made up in some form or other, for the main scale—(1-inch, 1/50,000 or 1/1,000,000). Most European maps of a smaller scale (¼-inch, 1/200,000, 1/300,000) use (1), (2) and (5), or omit the (5).

In Great Britain we are peculiarly fond both of contours and layers. Some of the 1-inch tourist maps are contoured and layered. There is a layered edition of the ½-inch. The modern ¼-inch, 10-mile and 1/M are all layered.

In one alternative form of the 5th edition of the 1-inch (the Relief, in red covers) and in certain special ½-inch sheets all methods are used. The contours are given to 50 feet intervals. They include therefore the surveyed and the interpolated. Next the hachures are given in soft brown, to bring up minor features. On top of that is a shadow plate made up by using the portions of the hachures which fall on the shadow side and printing them again in purple. Then to pick out high ground; to keep the plateau above the valley; a very simple layer system is added.

But there will always be some, perhaps many, who prefer unaided contouring. For them the other form of the 5th edition (in blue covers) avoids any attempt to help by colour.

It is as well to avoid contrasting the theoretical merits of the various systems too much. Contours are only accurate if they are made so, hill shading and hachuring only helpful if done with great care, layers only good if not too generalized. Let each man get what suits his purpose.

CHAPTER IX

Sections and Panoramas

WHAT part of the lock, to which this modest volume claims to be the key, can be humoured into action by sections and panoramas? The clue lies in those charming little panoramas which are given on the charts (look at St. Helena or Ascension Island) and in the sections of solid geology given on the geological maps. They amplify the maps they accompany. Maps are themselves a key to country, and the understanding of the ground itself is the real subject.

Plate II shows a part of the north coast of Somerset —the Doone part of Exmoor forest—and Plate V the 50-foot contouring of the same area. On it a line AB cuts across the rugged coastal strip of this charming country. Let us make a section of it, from mean sea level just beyond Porlock to the seventeen hundreds near A (see fig. 7).

Firstly draw a horizontal line AB to represent the datum. At each end erect perpendiculars and divide them up in a height scale. The scale of AB is one inch to the mile. Make the scale of heights four times this (a convenient ratio for sections in Great Britain). The contour interval of 50 feet is then $\frac{50}{5280}$ multiplied by 4, or 0·038 of an inch. In such bold and steep country the 100-foot interval will do for most parts. Divide the uprights then into 7 parts of 0·075 of an inch respectively; and join equivalent points by lines parallel to AB. Next on a strip of paper laid along AB (on the map) tick off the 100-foot contours. Convey

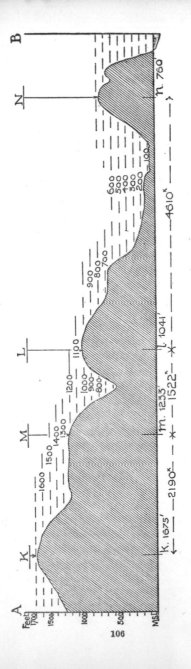

Fig. 7

PLATE V

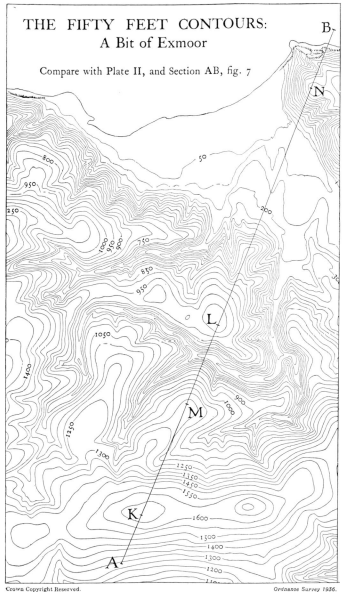

THE FIFTY FEET CONTOURS:
A Bit of Exmoor

Compare with Plate II, and Section AB, fig. 7

Ordnance Survey 1936.
facing p. 106

those ticks to the appropriate height lines of the section,
keeping A against one perpendicular, B against the
other. Draw the outline through the ticks and there is
your section complete.

Plate V shows no trees. The section may be supposed
for the moment to include all impediments (save those
of the atmosphere) to the view, and it solves at once
the problems of whether L is visible from K, or N from
M. Moreover it also shows just how much ground is
"dead" or hidden from any point you may choose on
the section line. This question of visibility is one much
used to test the intelligence of those who desire certi-
ficates of education. It may be solved, of course, on the
map itself without a section. Consider M and N and
find out whether the one can see the other or whether
L intervenes.

Stand at M. Now the gradient MN is the difference
of height divided by the distance between. Find it,
and find the gradient ML, and since you are going to
compare these you can measure heights and distances
in different units *if you do exactly the same in both cases.*

$$\text{Gradient MN} = \frac{1233 - 760}{6132} = \frac{473}{6132} \text{ or roughly I in 13.}$$

$$\text{ML} = \frac{1233 - 1041}{1522} = \frac{192}{1522} \text{ or roughly I in 8.}$$

The gradient ML is the steeper and the line ML dips,
therefore, below the line MN and will not interfere.
Obviously a matter of simple proportion. As a test of
mathematical skill this question, posed definitely, is
allowable. But geographically, and in the flatter parts
of England, let us pause. The error of an interpolated
contour may be (say) 10 feet, of estimating heights of
intermediate points (say) 25 feet, of hedgerow timber
(say) 60 feet, of the fences consider dates of normal
clipping, of buildings, spires, dumps and chimneys,
according to circumstances, and of the atmospheric

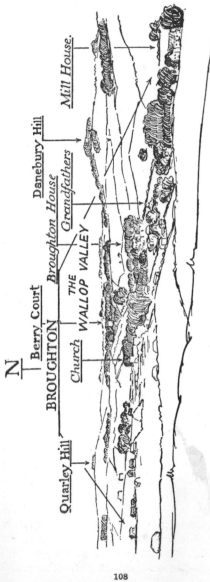

N

Quarley Hill

BROUGHTON

Berry Court

THE
WALLOP VALLEY

Church

Broughton House

Grandfathers

Danebury Hill

Mill House.

Fig. 8.—A Chalk Valley: height to distances as 2 to 1

108

visibility according to last night's weather forecast. Let us begin with " What are the chances?" and end by "Perhaps". However, this opens the door to an exercise under which many of us have suffered and from which we all profited immensely.

Select a point O on the map from which some sort of a view is certain. Draw a line up the centre of that view. On either side draw lines (say) at angles of 10°, with the centre line and with each other, radiating outwards into the field of view from O, so as to cover a total sector of 50°. Draw sections along those lines, establish what is visible and what is dead ground from O, and proceed to draw the country in the style of fig. 8. Make heights (say) twice the scale of distances. Next leave that finished drawing at home and proceed to the spot itself. There draw a panorama (fig. 8). Fig. 8 is pretty poor artistically, but correct enough in fact, and took 10 minutes in the field and 20 in an arm-chair. Proceed in this wise. Get a boxwood scale of any units you fancy (parasangs would do). Make a hole right in the centre, and thread a bit of string, with a knot at the end, through it. At about 12 to 18 inches from the scale tie on something to bite on (an indiarubber ring may awaken early memories). Holding on with the teeth, extend the string and look at the country and the scale together. Select your datum line (more or less equal in height to your own position). Measure along it horizontally to one or two key points (a hill, a spire, a house, and so on) from a selected centre point. Jot these horizontal measurements down on your datum line on the sketching paper. Turn the ruler into the vertical position. Measure heights of key points above and below the datum line. Plot them at twice the former scale. Make a skeleton of some dozen points in this way and then put in the rest by eye.

Return home triumphant and see why your original map-deduced panorama was all wrong. Having thus

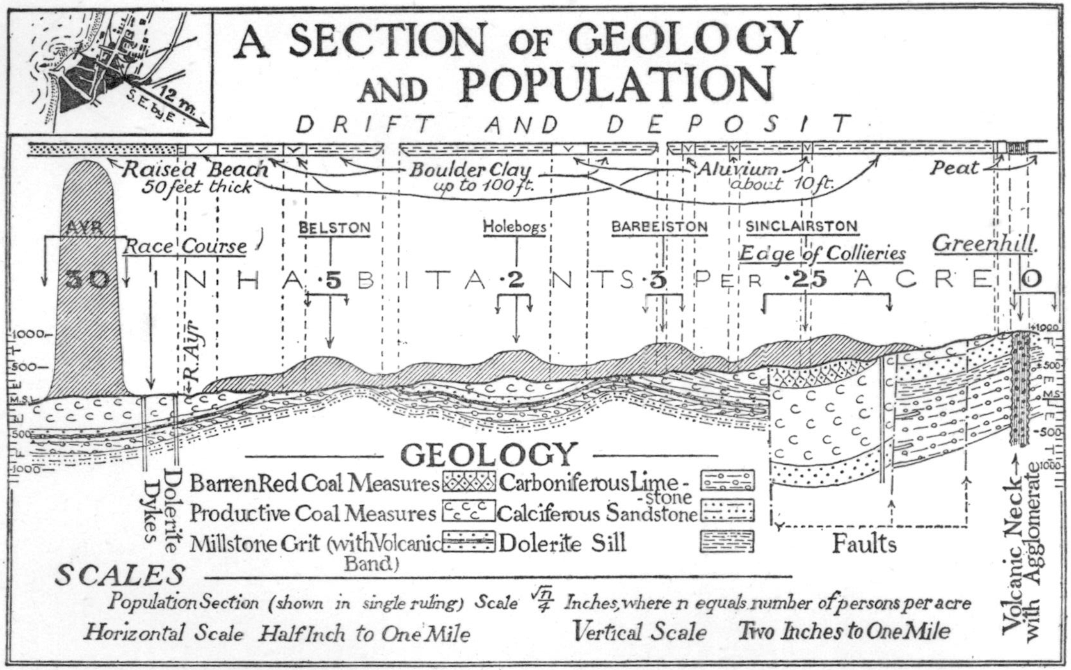

A SECTION OF GEOLOGY AND POPULATION

DRIFT AND DEPOSIT

Raised Beach 50 feet thick

Boulder Clay up to 100ft.

Alluvium about 10ft.

Peat

Holebogs

Race Course

AYR

R. Ayr

BELSTON

BAREISTON

SINCLAIRSTON

Greenhill

Edge of Collieries

INHABITANTS · 5 · 2 · 3 · ·25 · PER ·5 ACRE · O

·30

Volcanic Neck with Agglomerate

Dolerite Dykes

Faults

GEOLOGY

Barren Red Coal Measures

Productive Coal Measures

Millstone Grit (with Volcanic Band)

Carboniferous Lime-stone

Calciferous Sandstone

Dolerite Sill

SCALES

Population Section (shown in single ruling) Scale $\sqrt[n]{2}$ Inches, where n equals number of persons per acre

Horizontal Scale Half Inch to One Mile

Vertical Scale Two Inches to One Mile

Fig. 9

110

learnt humility, lock both away resolutely. Take half an hour over something else, and then sit down and draw it all again from memory! You will be surprised at the result. The chances are that gentle hills will swell to Everests, that you will bring your distances into the foreground, and that you will have taught yourself something of that knowledge of " what happens behind the hill " known as an eye for country.

Everyone interested both in man and the country in which he lives is at once a budding geographer, and a budding socialist (within reason!) Sections can be applied to all sorts of problems connecting the two. See fig. 9 which illustrates the rise and fall of the country, the development, the geology solid and drift, and the population, along a line S.E. from Ayr. Observe that any number of additional subjects could be treated. On the population section (whose datum is the topographical outline) could be superimposed one of religious difference, or of average height, or political persuasion, or of the prevalence of lumbago. The figure explains itself, however, and no more will be said.

Those who wish to pursue Field Sketching are advised to consult the *Manual of Map-reading, Photo-reading and Field Sketching*, 1929, War Office, H.M.S.O. 3s.

CHAPTER X

Locating Oneself

IT is curious to notice how universal is the sense of direction and distance among Africans generally. No doubt all more or less primitive peoples, who have never been cramped up in cities, enjoy this characteristic. It cannot be inherited, however, even in their case, and must be acquired through an active open-air life. Amongst us, as a people, the sense of direction, the " eye for country " varies very greatly, but it can always be acquired, though never out of books. There are some whom we cannot imagine at a loss, people who after the first visit that way will follow the most devious paths without a check. No doubt this is due more to subconscious, than to conscious, observation. That curious chimney, the wind-bent trees on this bit of down, the snug-looking "Nelson's Arms", the sharp gradient which ends in a particular view, the line of the electric pylons, and more important than all the fact that one turns south, or east, at a particular place. Such an one will require no hints on direction from this chapter, which is written for those whose " eye for country " has still to be developed. To the latter, let me say at once that a little practice will make it well-nigh impossible to lose one's way in Great Britain except in fog or mist. On the other hand it is of value sometimes to identify an exact position, and to record (say) where to find a particular flower, or outcrop, and here even the expert wanderer may be glad of a hint.

Approximate Sun Methods.

Let us start by assuming, for the moment, that the forecast of " visibility fair to good " has been accurate. The easiest guide to approximate direction is the sun. Owing to the curious angle of that axis, round which the earth revolves, the sun is not likely to be exactly due south at noon. But that is a matter of indifference in map-reading, because it is as near it as we want to "set" the map for that purpose. Again, at Lowestoft, on the one hand, or Mallaig, on the other, we are, obviously, getting away from the Greenwich meridian and sun time will be earlier or later than our watches in consequence. But this matter too is of no importance in ordinary map-reading. The expert who has his tables and his logarithm book or slide-rule can, of course, obtain an exact answer. For those who are not experts, the sun is a help but not a precise guide.

The easiest way, if the sun is shining, is to use your watch. Supposing the hour is 4 o'clock. Hold the watch flat, and directly under your eye, and point the hour hand at the sun itself. Then true north is half-way between that and 12 o'clock on your watch dial, and looking from the centre of your watch towards 2 o'clock will mean that you are looking towards the south. But here, of course, is an obvious snag. Outdoor holidays are mostly in the summer, and then summer time applies. The time we actually use is an hour ahead of that which is normal for the sun. Harking back to the last illustration, in summer if your watch says 4 o'clock you must so hold your watch that from the centre of it towards 3 is in the direction of the sun. Half-way between that and 12 will give you the south, which, therefore, will be towards half-past one on your watch's dial.

After going through this routine once or twice it will be found just as simple to set off an angle from the sun by eye. The sun may be taken to move across about 15 degrees an hour (although this is, of course, the roughest approximation).

At ten in the morning, then, true south would be roughly 30 degrees west of the sun's position. Hold out an arm towards the sun and revolve it through some 30 degrees westwards and lay the map out by that orientation. This rough sun guide will not serve in the early mornings or late evenings. The sun is then moving upwards and downwards more than across. In fact it is only between 8 a.m. and 4 p.m. that the rough rules given above may be held to apply well enough. A little practice in the use of the sun as a direction finder may pass an interesting five minutes or so. It can be tested easily too in this way. Get a penny and drop some sealing wax on it. Then stick a pencil upright on the sealing wax. Put it on a sheet of paper, which is lying flat in the sunlight, and make a ring round the position of the penny. Take an hour before midday, and an hour after it, and mark the shadows cast by the pencil. Then half-way between is true south and the angles of travel for an hour can be measured. Amongst the South African natives, the comparative accuracy of time forecasting: " When the sun be there, Boss "—(accompanied by a pointing finger)—is remarkable, and time is only another name for direction. I must reiterate, however, that setting a map in order to identify surroundings need never be more than " approximate ", and that a sheet of paper looked at from anywhere above (not on a table with a straightedge) is not susceptible of any fine angular measurement, nor is that accuracy in the least bit necessary for ordinary work.

Accurate Star Methods.

Supposing that night has fallen: the sun is no longer there to see, and the Great Bear has twinkled out to give us aid instead. Two consecutive positions of the Great Bear, which revolves round the pole anti-clockwise, are shown in fig. 10. Polaris (or the pole star) is not always visible even if the Great Bear is. It may be taken to lie along the line of the pointers and roughly five times the distance between the pointers from the last of the latter. Polaris is always within two degrees of true North.

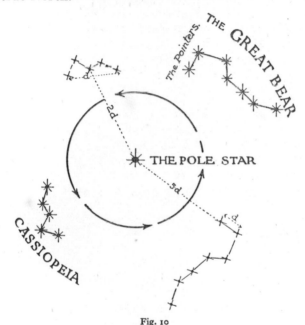

Fig. 10

On a cloudy night it is possible that the Great Bear may vanish but that Cassiopeia may still be there, in the form of a badly designed W on the other side of the pole star. It is not very easy to describe exactly how to locate the pole star from Cassiopeia. The figure must serve. Remember, however, that the pole star is about twice the distance between the outside top points of the W as measured from the middle of the line joining them.

Supposing that fate calls you south of the equator. The Great Bear, dropping lower and lower in the sky, has at last vanished. Unfamiliar heavens grow upon you, and at length you will see the Southern Cross. There is romance in the sound of it, but not quite so much help, for it is not so conspicuous. It is a constellation of four stars outlining the extremities of the ordinary (as opposed to the Maltese) Cross.

It is not itself at the south pole but revolves round it, and because you will then be looking south, having turned about, the apparent rotation is clockwise. The distance of the pole is four and a half times the length of the longer arm of the cross from the point which marks its lower (and southern) end. Mark off twelve equal spaces on the edge of a piece of paper. Hold it up until divisions one and three are opposite the head and tail stars of the longer arm; then division twelve will be opposite the south pole, but there is no visible star there to give the exact spot.

The Compass.

By day visibility may, however, still be good even if the sun refuses to shine. Indeed there is no better visibility than under blue cloud in a rain exhausted sky, and here we come to the compass.

At one time, no doubt, the compass needle must have seemed a miraculous affair and have been implicitly trusted. Custom has staled that early admiration—at any rate for the surveyor. It is, however, an excellent friend to him who wanders with a map. The poles to which the needle bears witness are not the north and south poles. They are the ends of an axis which runs at an angle to that of the earth's rotation and they appear to lie within the earth, for a free needle suspended on a thread will point downwards as well as northwards. This "dip" is eliminated in the ordinary compass, so we may forget all about it. The magnetic poles are restless affairs. They cannot be tied down except on some given date and time, because they are for ever changing position a little with reference to true (geographical) north and south. This movement is composed really of two; a slow and (over a year or so) fairly consistent one, and another minor daily one. The daily one is, however, small and again we may forget all about it. The slow change affects the angle between true north and magnetic north (an angle which is sometimes called the variation and sometimes the declination) in the same direction for many years, although each year the rate of change may vary. Obviously this angle between the two norths must alter with the position of the observer. The right figure for Aberdeen is not that for Purbeck. One can imagine being at an unpleasantly cold spot such that the magnetic pole would be exactly opposite to the north pole and that the south end of the compass would point to the latter. For all practical purposes, however, you are saved by the information given in the eastern margin of the map. Here is a north point all complete with the variation of a certain year (the date of the last publication of that sheet) given in figures and completed by a statement of how much the yearly change is likely to be. The declination (or variation) is not to be applied to the sheet lines (which are not true north and south), but the margin of the map explains all that too. Now let us examine the compass. The needle itself is not singleminded in its attentions to the magnetic poles. Anything which is magnetic will affect it, attract it, or repel it. There may be, for all you know, underlying mineral rocks perhaps half a mile under where you stand, which may visibly affect it. To get the bearing of a railway line is obviously a hazardous affair and the only hope is to stand so exactly between the rails that the uncertain needle may remember its duty, and point to the north.

I knew a man who desired greatly to obtain a magnetic bearing but whose efforts proved fantastic;

unbelievable indeed; until it transpired that he wore a truss. A mine surveyor confided in me that before using a miner's dial (a large compass) he always removed his braces. For map-reading we need run no such risks, but it is as well to remember spectacles (and the case) and knives, and any loose iron or steel about you. The next point of importance is the pivot upon which the needle turns. This pivot is rather likely to suffer from wear. Indeed it is quite remarkable how many are faulty, and introduce such friction as to make the needle come to rest before it has reached the proper end of its swing. The test is very simple. Get a soft iron nail or some such object and approach it quickly to the compass. See if it pulls the needle quickly from the north, and whether the needle returns as quickly when the nail is removed, and, moreover, reads the same as it did before. Try it on the other side of the compass and finally test a map-bearing or two to see if the needle has any particular bias. Some of them have. Satisfied now with instrument, and confident in the knowledge of what to avoid, put the compass on the north point of the map (in the eastern margin). Rotate the map until magnetic north and the compass agree, and the map is " set ".

Straight Lines.

Now, however, we must begin to realize that in most cases neither sun, star nor compass is necessary at all. In 1824 General Colby (the greatest Director-General the Ordnance Survey has known) was giving evidence on the unreliability of contemporary land surveying. He stated that he would never accept its results without thorough examination on the ground. He was asked how he would conduct that examination and replied: " We should walk over it (the country) and observe if those objects which were in a line in the country were also in a line on the map. . . ." But the maps we now have are exceedingly good. If two

points are in a line in the country they are so on the
map, and naturally the converse applies. This is the
principle on which map revision rests (see fig. 17,
Chapter XVI) and it is the normal procedure of the
yachtsman who depends on compass and parallel
ruler. Such an one talks of a "straight", by which he
means the line which joins two points on the map or
chart. Directly he gets on to that straight, orientation
follows at once. He and the two points are then on
one straight line which is mapped at its proper angle
to true north. Somewhere on that line is the position
of the moment and if a ruler or any moderately straight
object (such as the edge of an envelope) is laid on that
line and then turned (map and all) round to coincide
with the ground, the map is set. In England
generally and many parts of Scotland this simple
procedure is possible and very easy. One has to look
round the country for any remarkable objects which
can be identified on the map. Identify the two which
are nearest to defining a line through your position,
and then walk this way or that until you are on the
line.

Sometimes ground and map provide a ready-made
line. For example a railway "straight" (such as
appears on fig. 11) is just as good as two points. A
Roman road or a line of pylons may serve just as well.
Perhaps too *you* can provide the bearing if the ground
and map provide one visible and identifiable point.
Supposing that a distant spire is just visible above
the lift of the down, or the hedgerows of flat country.
Take a compass bearing to it; add 180 degrees to
make it read from, and not to, the spire and plot it
(not forgetting variation) backwards towards you.
You are on that line, and it is more than probable
that the clue so provided will enable you to find your
map position.

So far all the talk has been of orientation or setting,
and none about fixing position. Let us now follow out

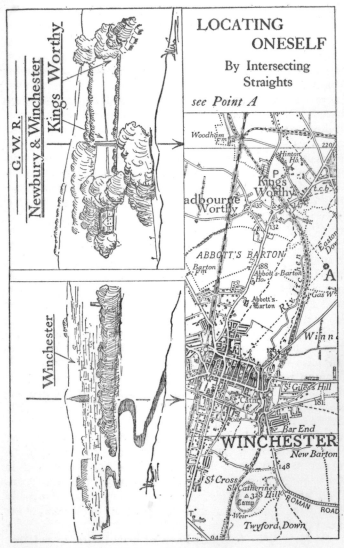

Fig. 11

120

the last method and use it for finding position. That merely entails two straights instead of one. See fig. 11 which illustrates the idea. Having got on one straight, walk along it, in either direction (i.e. towards or away from the nearest of the first pair of points) until you come to where another "straight", preferably at right angles, cuts the first. The whole problem is now solved, for two straight lines clamped down on the earth can meet in only one place which will interest you (the other, you know, is somewhere about Australia, see p. 36).

Resection.

Most books on map-reading make much of "resection". But in reality resection is seldom necessary in Great Britain except perhaps in wide open spaces, such as Rannoch Muir, Teesdale, or the east of Sutherlandshire. There is so much shown on the normal map that the method of straights will serve, or even an orientation will show one so nearly where the position is that it may be measured up from fence or road. Resection is done thus.

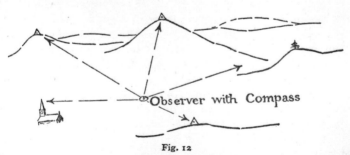

Fig. 12

The observer takes compass readings to four or five points. Here the mathematician will object, for in theory three are enough, but that is only providing that you are sure of your three points and can lay an unerring pencil on the same positions on the map as you choose in the landscape. For most of us in strange country that is an unwarrantable assumption. Best take five. Then with a protractor (do you always carry one?) plot these on the tracing paper which you have thoughtfully brought along. Place the tracing paper on the map and shuffle it about until the lines pass well and truly through the map positions of the points. You will then be at the nodal point (that from which the bearings radiate).

Tracing paper resection of the sort outlined above is not very satisfactory. To get the right spot, lines should be very clear and thin, the points observed on should be sharply defined and the plotting of the compass bearings as accurate as possible. It is better to resect on the map as explained below, but the method necessitates a piece of board on which to pin the map flat, a dozen or more additional pins, and a really straight cane (or stick), or, better, a boxwood or metal scale.

First of all identify three well-marked points on the ground which are also clearly defined on the map. Pinning the map on the board, place pins also in the three " witness " map points. Place the map as level as possible on a rock or tussock of grass, so as to be able to get the eye to the level of the map. Now " set " the map as nearly as you can by compass (or sun). Point the ruler at one of the witness points, keeping one edge of it against the pin (representing that point on the map). Draw a line from the pin towards yourself. Repeat the process from the other two witness point pins, pointing the ruler at the points on the ground. Then the three lines will form " a triangle of error ", unless luck intervenes and they all intersect in a point, which would mean unexpected success at the first try. The next step is to reduce the triangle of error to a point. There are two rules to remember:

1. If you are inside the triangle formed by the three points on the ground then your map position is inside

the triangle of error. If you are outside the triangle
on the ground, you are outside the triangle of error.

2. The correct position is nearest to the shortest
ray (that from the nearest point) and farthest from the
longest ray.

Considering those two rules, put a pin into the position you think indicated. Now orient along the two pins
which represent the position of the farthest witness point
and that of your assumed position—by placing the
ruler against them and slightly rotating the map till
it points truly at the farthest point. Draw a very small
bit of the ray on either side of the position pin. Then
pointing the ruler at the other two witness points
(placing its edge against their pins and neglecting the
" position " pin) draw rays from them. If the rules
have been correctly followed you will get either a
good intersection or a much reduced triangle of error.
If the latter, try again. When the correct position has
been found test it by orienting first on the farthest of
the three original witness points and then revolving
the ruler to point at some well-defined fourth point. If
that cuts the correct position on the map, all is well.
If not, you have failed to identify one of the three
original witness points on the map. Use a hardish
pencil, with as sharp a point as you can make.

The wisdom of taking five points is now apparent.
If four are correct and one ray will not pass through
its place on the map, then you are at once sure of
position and convinced that in one case you have
failed to reconcile country and map.

In Bad Visibility.

All the situations mentioned so far have, however,
postulated visibility. The real trouble comes when one
cannot see; when thick fog, dripping mist, or cloudy
darkness makes everything invisible a few feet away.
The first point is this. Do not embark on a walk which
is like to end under such conditions, until you have

studied the map carefully, or without a small electric torch and a luminous compass. With these to aid the map one may confidently expect to reach home betimes.

If there is no torch, the dwindling box of matches or the emptying petrol lighter will have to serve, and instead of the compass it is possible that the wind may help, although, in England, it is generally very variable. Wet the inside of your forefinger (a real good lick) and hold it above your head. Turn it slowly round till it suddenly cools as the breeze dries it. In this fashion does the small-boat sailor watch for his breeze. If you are really lost the direction of the wind may at least keep you, for a time, from walking, as many do, in a circle. Long ago, at the battle of Paardeberg to be exact, a captain and a subaltern were tramping the weary way to bivouac after a night of trench digging. The captain began to circle and the subaltern, with a muttered appeal to a broken bootlace, dropped to cover behind an ant-heap. The captain was swallowed up in darkness and it was the subaltern who ate what was available of supper. Many of us, do, in fact, tend to step farther with one foot than the other.

If really and thoroughly lost start with a chuckle at your own stupidity. Having thus calmed the troubled mind spend five minutes in going over the clues. An hour ago, or ten minutes ago, the approximate situation was plain. What has happened since? Take out the map, illuminate it for a good long stare. Have you been walking uphill or down, crossed a stream, glimpsed a lake, seen the light of a cottage or walked into trees? Illuminate again and see if your memory and the map may show a common clue. Then taking the best direction you can, stick to that line. If you fall into a really remarkable ditch or obstacle you will be in luck's way. It will probably be on the map.

CHAPTER XI

Locating a Point

ADVENTURERS, explorers, and those whose travels take both them and their audiences far afield, generally refer to the position of a place, or a camp, as being at such and such a latitude and longitude. We can then look it up, with a little trouble, in an atlas. Obviously, however, we should not dream of directing a friend to find us at home at a latitude and longitude. Lines which are not parallel, or at right angles, to each other are clumsy for quick reference and do not lend themselves to that division by eye which one demands of such a system. For years, then, no one has attempted to make a popular gazetteer in terms of latitude and longitude.

Most maps, and the gazetteers (if any) which accompany them, depend upon a system of squares. The surface of the map is divided up into rows of squares, labelled *a*, *b*, *c*, *d*, &c., in the east and west margins, and 1, 2, 3, 4, &c., in the north and south margins. This is the system of the popular edition of the ordnance 1-inch, and of contemporary ½- and ¼-inch editions. Square *b*5, or *a*2, is easily found and somewhere within this square lies the point or position we are looking for. Many valuable indexes have been made on these maps and by this system. For example, the English Place Name Society has recorded a mass of valuable information in this way. It is the common practice of guide books and town plans to index names in the same way. In a guide book, for example, a reference

would be " map " or " folio " 11, $c7$, and in square $c7$
of map 11 the place is to be found. There is simplicity
and ease of reference in this system, but unfortunately
two drawbacks.

The first is the size of square. Everyone, I suspect,
has had experience of searching over a square, crowded
with small names, for the place he wants to find. The
reference narrows down the search to an area and not
to a point.

The second is even more important. The reference is
based on something quite temporary. Supposing that
an index had been made, say of inns, or antiquities, of
historic castles or of the nesting places of a certain
bird, on Mudge's first 1-inch map, by this system,
which depends upon the unaltered position of sheet
lines. Since that day the sheet lines have been altered
six times. We should now be using a sixth edition, and
every edition would have cost a lot of time, since the
reference to every item would require change. Supposing all six to have been well and truly made, none
would be of any value to the man with a " district "
sheet (different sheet lines again), nor would any ½-inch
or ¼-inch map assist, for they too would have different
sheet lines. Maps *will* change to meet the convenience
of the times and no system has a chance of permanency
which is based upon their size and margins.

Another system sometimes employed requires a
strip of printed linen, hinged somewhere to the margin.
Those I have seen generally hinge the strip in the centre
of the western margin. Round the edges of the map
are given bearings, on the " tangent scale " principle,
divided from 0° to 180°. The strip itself carries
some arbitrary scale of distances, reading outwards
from the hinge. The reference would be 111° (revolve
the linen strip to the point 111° on the tangent scale)
137 (measure along strip to division 137). " Polar Co-
ordinates " is the mathematical description, and in
theory perfectly easy and quick. In practice, the linen

strip is a terrible nuisance, and this too is a system which can be applied only to one given map. It has never been employed on official maps and is, obviously, unpopular.

With regard to permanency, it does seem time that we got used to a system which will safeguard the labours of statisticians and others and make their references intelligible whatever changes may occur in the form or scale of maps. With regard to convenience it is time so to plan that system that anyone can, with ease, find the exact place or name without a tiresome search. A system embodying these two points has recently appeared on the fifth edition of the 1-inch and on all new small-scale maps, and will now be explained.

As in the $a7$ principle described above the maps are covered with lines which, in effect, form squares, although that fact is not important. But these lines are not necessarily drawn with any reference to the sheet lines of the map. They are lines at definite and specified distances north and east of a certain spot on the earth. Any map, at any scale, can show these lines. The spot on the earth (or rather in the sea!) is a million yards south and a million yards west of the origin of the official map construction. In spreading measurement over the country one has to start from somewhere. For survey purposes the " origin " is 49° north and 2° west, and is well inside England, but then for trained computers plus and minus signs have no terror. By adding a million each way all minus signs, in the reference, are avoided.

The reference to any given spot is, then, so many yards east and so many yards north, and is always given in that order so that the words east and north are unnecessary. To find out how many yards east one has to refer to the north or south margins of the map and to select that line which is nearest to the point (but on the west of it), and then to measure and add the yards from that line. To find how far north one consults the east and west margins and chooses the line nearest (but south), measuring and adding the final distance. In practice this procedure comes to finding the point and identifying the south-west corner of the square or rectangle in which it lies. Take the easterly distance of the south-west corner and add the remaining distance east, then take the northerly distance of that same south-west corner and add the remaining distance north, and the reference is complete.

It is quite remarkable how easy references are to give and to understand on this principle, but in practice the final measurement is generally made by eye and given only to a reasonable figure. On the 1-inch scale 1000 yards is not much more than half an inch, 100 yards about one-sixteenth of an inch. For some purposes references will be given to 100 yards, but for many others the nearest 1000 yards will suffice. For example, if the reference is to enable someone else to find a name on a 1-inch map of open country, it need not be more detailed than 1000 yards each way, although on (say) the 3-inch to the mile of London it should read to 100 yards. On the 1-inch a reference meant to fix a meeting-place would do well to read to the nearest 100 yards.

The lines which define distances east and north, and the squares they form, differ, naturally, on the different scales. On the 1-inch they are 5000 yards apart or nearly 3 inches. On the ½-inch these same lines, less than 1½ inches from each other, would be a real interference with the map, and so they are 10,000 yards apart. On the 3-inch of London they are 1000 yards apart. These distances are not material however. The numbered lines are just so many conveniences: the system remains the same.

Supposing we take the position of the Albert Memorial, which is, to be accurate, 1,138,500, 1,306,000. The position thus located can be found, within the limits of the scale, on a 3-inch, 1-inch, $\frac{1}{2}$-inch, $\frac{1}{4}$-inch, or 10-mile (all now published on this system in London), whether the scale of the map allows the Memorial to be actually shown or not. Suppose, in the future, that some traveller has lost his way, map notwithstanding, on a lonely road, and eventually reaches a signpost. Suppose that on that signpost are its co-ordinates or reference figures. Then whatever map he carries (if it has this system on it), he will be immediately placed and can go on his way rejoicing.

Ease of referencing will naturally lead to the omission of a number of the figures. If, for example, we are not particular as to the units or tens, but refer only to the hundreds, then we can omit the last two figures. If again we are (and know that we are) referring to a part lying near London or Glasgow or any other centre, we can omit many of the earlier figures. No rule can be laid down yet, because we have not had the system working long enough; but the London 3-inch provides an excellent illustration of simplification. In the corners the full co-ordinates are given, but against each line are printed only two figures. Thus 50 (east) really means 1,150,000. The next line east is 51. Any point to be located (generally by eye) as $\frac{8}{10}$ of the distance from 50 to 51 will naturally be 508. The gazetteer which accompanies the map gives, in fact, only six figures—three east and three north. It is in regard to this map that a social worker, who has to visit many remote streets every day, writes:

" For the very reason that I am not good at maps I never wish to use any in future save those printed with co-ordinates. To search a square on a map may take five minutes, to find a reference on this map not a minute."

It is often convenient to measure and record with the help of a small card. Eye estimation is generally good enough in "reading"; or in finding the place referred to in an index or gazetteer; but it is often important to be much more accurate in making the reference. In compiling an index, for example, a card measurer must be used. They are extremely easy to make. The scale of yards on the bottom margin of the map will provide the correct distances on the scale used. Any square cornered piece of paper—say an old envelope —will then do for the card. It is, however, just as easy to make it of stout cardboard, or a piece of three-ply (with two edges bevelled). During the War many of us used pieces of zinc, which, however, had the drawback of oversharp corners. It is far easier to illustrate a card than to describe it, and therefore please look at Plate VI, which shows one designed to act for the four scales—1-inch, $\frac{1}{2}$-inch, $\frac{1}{4}$-inch, and 10-mile. It is possible that it may seem a little too complicated for ordinary use (although it isn't really in practice). If so, confine the card to one scale at a time. Notice that it reads (apparently) backwards, but that is just to make it easy to put the corner of the card on the exact spot you are interested in, and then read the correct answer *against* the nearest lines west and south. Stanford's sell a useful little co-ordinate card for a shilling.

It will be interesting, presently, to see what help the 1-inch gazetteers give. Each sheet has its gazetteer of all the place names on it. When all these are finished and collected, all the places concerned will be so indexed that they can be found in a moment or two on any scale map.

It is unlikely that the plans, as well as the maps, will have these references, for eye referencing is not important for plans rarely used out of doors. On the plans refer to the plan number, the " parcel " number if the spot is in a field, or, if not, in relation to the nearest name—as, for example:

" $1\frac{1}{2}$ inches south of the *u* in Buckholt "

PLATE VI

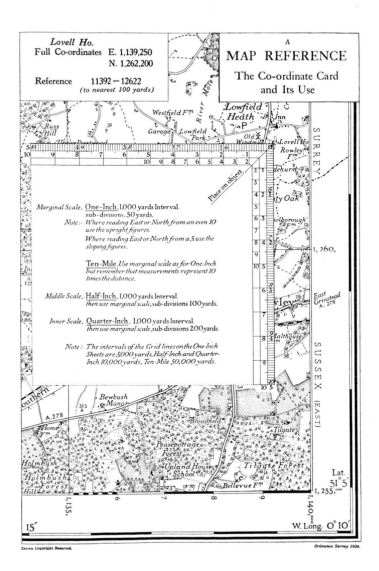

Ordnance Survey 1936.

CHAPTER XII

Sheet Lines, Covers, and Folds

RIGID systems of sheet lines, so often fatal to convenience, came to us in Great Britain amongst other early Victorian tidinesses. They had been characteristic of Cassini's map of France, and we have record of Napoleon, busily planning German campaigns, sitting over map indexes and fixing sheet lines with his staff officers. In England maps had generally been of counties and bore in the margin the coats of arms of county magnates, which were, of course, highly ornamental. When Mudge began to publish the first 1-inch he still had this county principle in mind. It was soon given up on that scale, but even to-day it is still common to hear of the twenty-five plans as " the county maps ". Mudge's maps were large in size, about 33 × 29 inches. They were not regarded, it would seem, as documents for field use, at any rate outside a tent.

Then came the changes which are natural to a consistent national series. Progress is bound to be retarded by publication in curious corners and odd bits, such as are implied by county boundaries, and therefore sheets were produced in rectangular sheet lines and numbered consecutively. For a time the convenience of field use was still forgotten and sheets were designed to be 36 × 24 inches. Field convenience at a period before linen backing and folding in covers, meant a small map. Besides, as most travel by foot or horseback was slow, a large area was not required. For these reasons the last of the " old series " and all the " new " were produced in quarter sheets 18 inches by a foot in size.

These small sheets led to all sorts of inconvenience on the edges. The Brighton sheet, for example, came, on the index, as a strip of coast, and as a strip of coast just including Brighton, it remained. All sorts of stupidities of that sort occurred. Towns were cut in half, or were separated from their natural play grounds. We all know how often now we are on the edge of a sheet, to our dismay, just when the map is becoming important, but with the rigidity of those days and the smallness of the sheets the discomfort was far worse. This discomfort led to a determined attack on our sheet line policy during a committee of 1892 and it was decided to issue a lot of district maps, considerably larger in size, and specially designed to serve local purposes. By that time the survey was done and plates were made. It was relatively simple to begin a policy of making the maps more helpful, and the sheet lines more human.

The issue of larger sheets started the folding and covering (in 1902). Our first covers were peculiarly official brown affairs with a " take it or leave it " atmosphere about them. By filling in the appropriate form in a post office and then waiting on official convenience, you could obtain them from the Ordnance Survey.

At this moment a new edition of the 1-inch was in progress and the sheets adopted the larger areas now becoming popular. The size selected was one of 27 × 18 inches. Starting in 1912 and finishing in 1919, it covered England and Wales in 152 sheets.

The " Popular " edition was the next to appear. The sheet lines were again altered, but the size remained the same. Indeed, for one reason or another, sheet lines seem

to be liable to perpetual change. This edition was
begun before the Great War, but was very much held
up by it, and no sheets appeared before 1919. The
last sheet of Scotland was not in fact printed until
1932. Scotland generally sees a new idea, however,
because the march of revision, from Land's End to
the Shetland Islands, gives time to try out the new
editions in England and Wales, and to be ready for
minor changes when the border is reached. One of
those changes during the progress of the popular editions
was the introduction of an overlap between sheets.
Thus each sheet covers a strip of 2 inches already
included in the sheet to the south, and a similar overlap into the sheet to the east. Even so, however, many
holiday areas were scurvily treated, and throughout
its lifetime regular sheets of this edition were accompanied by an increasing number of district and tourist
maps. Some of these would be too big for normal
convenience. For example the " Lakes " special sheet
is no less than 24 × 30 inches.

The fifth edition is now well on its way. The sheets
are 29½ × 17 inches, but vary sometimes in awkward
spots, and the district and tourist maps continue to
appear. The overlap, this time north and east, continues
too. It is obvious that sheet lines have not yet become
quite human. There are many who are still in a corner,
and many places and neighbourhoods of interest
which are divided up in arbitrary fashion. Perhaps the
clue to follow is to have two complementary editions—
an A series with sheets of about the present size, and a
B series each sheet of which will include a quarter of
the four surrounding A sheets. Most of us would then
be happy and special " districts " and " tourists "
might disappear. Meanwhile, do not be content with
a sheet which divides your front garden from your
back. There may well be a " district " or a " tourist ".
If the Ordnance Survey cannot satisfy try some of
the numerous others. There are, of course, map col-

lectors who acquire the whole of a series. But they are in no need of assistance.

A ½-inch scale lends itself better to the special sheet idea. There are but seventy-four of them for Great Britain. At present, however, they are as arbitrary as the 1-inch. Five special sheets—the London and Birmingham areas, the Cotswolds, the Peak District, and the Isle of Skye—are of exceptional interest. For the rest those who delight in this scale must ring the changes between the various map-makers and find that one suited to their purpose.

The ¼-inch grows and grows in the size of sheet. A shortish while ago, one could not use a single sheet to go from Edinburgh to Glasgow or from Leeds to Manchester. Now the ¼-inch, readjusting here and adding there, is growing in understanding and almost ceasing to be a " regular series ". To join them up would require many cuts. The largest sheet is 21½ × 32½ inches.

The 10-mile illustrates the change of thought in sheet lines very clearly. The first edition had 12 sheets of 20 × 13 inches. A " C " series, combining some by cutting off large strips of sea and joining up, reduced the number of sheets to eight. A new edition, begun in 1922, reduced that number to three, with considerable overlaps, at a size of 38 × 26 inches. In this edition, however, Scotland was cut in half, and subsequent adjustments made the Scottish sheet complete, leaving two sheets to cover England. A recent edition on the " Ansell fold " gives the whole of Great Britain in one map.

The original 1/M, a beautifully engraved map, was produced in two sheets, each 24½ × 34¾ inches. Then came the international 1/M map which very naturally displaced its predecessor. Unfortunately international sheet lines cut up Great Britain into seven sheets. For national use these sheets have been combined into two, just as Denmark, cut into two by the international convention, has combined them into one for local sale.

Regular or district, 1-inch, ½-inch, ¼-inch or 10-mile, all are alike in that the sheet lines are not true north and south. In the days of county series each sheet was plotted on its own meridian. Sheet lines would be truly north and south. Now the map of Great Britain is one complete map and the sheets are simply portions cut out, so to speak, with a ruler. Great Britain has its central meridian and the ruler, cutting out lines parallel to it, diverges further from the converging meridians (they must all meet at the north pole!) as the cutting out nears the extremes of east and west.

In the outside world rectangular sheet lines are the exception and not the rule. Each sheet is, generally, an item of latitude and longitude. The sheets join up uneasily, if at all, and holiday areas are not often catered for, though they sometimes are.

The sheet lines of the plans are simple to grasp and are not subject to the rapid changes characteristic of the smaller scales. When the system was first designed each county had its own meridian and origin. Sheet lines developed as lines at right angles, and parallel, to that county meridian. The first counties in England to have a large-scale survey were finished on the scale of 6 inches to a mile (Lancashire and Yorkshire) and therefore the 6-inch sheets, numbered consecutively throughout the county, became the guiding factor. A 6-inch sheet of those days was 36×24 inches (covering 24 square miles). Then after long discussion the 25-inch (1/2500) was adopted, and the area of the 6-inch divided into 16 sheets for the larger scale. These are also numbered consecutively as 1 to 16, starting in the north-west corner and running from left to right.

Now comes a modification to the 6-inch. At first this scale was reduced by hand from the 25-inch and redrawn. By this time the camera had begun to be an active help, although at first the accuracy of photo-

graphic reductions had been doubted.   However, a
special committee, appointed by the War Office to
investigate the matter, reported favourably in 1859,
and photographic reduction was officially sanctioned.
Unfortunately the camera of those days was small,
and would not cover an area greater than that repre-

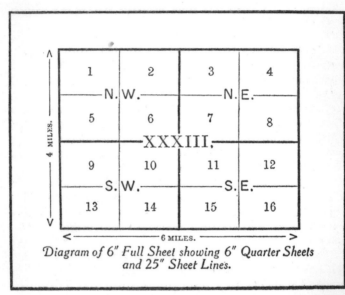

*Diagram of 6" Full Sheet showing 6" Quarter Sheets
and 25" Sheet Lines.*

Fig. 13—The Numbering of the Plans

sented by four complete 25-inch sheets.   The 6-inch
had, then, to be produced in four quarter sheets, each
18 × 12 inches.   A quarter sheet is listed as (say) Essex
25 N.E.   Curiously enough, this small size has survived
to the present day.   It is small, and for anyone interested
in large areas inconveniently so.   Yet the country
seems to desire this size, as was found by an investigation of 1923.   Perhaps as official responsibility grows
(as in the case of Town and Regional Planning) there
may be a call for the whole sheets again, and, as cameras

have grown in size and precision, the whole sheet is easily made to-day.

The map, once printed, is sent for finishing off, and the greater part of each edition is linen backed. The cheapest article is, of course, the "paper flat", and a perfectly good article it is, too, for those who want it for home use and have shelves or trays on which to store. But those two conditions are not often found in combination. It is a great mistake to buy unmounted maps for field use. One wet day and they are gone. The additional 9d. for "mounted and folded" is well spent. The covers too are a great convenience both indoors and out. There is not a little information on the covers, they keep the map relatively clean even in a pocket, and the title and number, made conspicuous on the front, help one to pick the right article out of the bookcase. They are not, of course, equal to all emergencies, as had to be pointed out to a climber in the Cuillins who had kept his two maps between a tin of sardines and a pair of dubbined boots, but they will serve, generally, as long as the map fulfils its purpose.

There are all sorts of ways of folding a map. Normally our British maps are longer east and west than they are north and south, a shape which is much the most convenient for field use. The best form of fold is in three from north to south, with the two covers at each end of the centre row. Then it is easy to leave out the top two-thirds or the bottom two-thirds. So folded the length of cover is about $7\frac{1}{2}$ inches. The map is then folded inwards in some eight sections, so as to give just over 4 inches across. Personally I prefer this type of cover to any, but, amongst motorists, there are those who can never remember the right way, lose it preferably in a hurricane, and find the map instinct with rebellion. For their benefit very long covers are now available for the $\frac{1}{4}$-inch. The map is simply folded into two, north and south, so that a

minimum of trouble is caused in opening it. But
these long covers raise the question of the study shelves.
Those who keep their maps in the house will prefer the
old style.

Supposing that you buy a foreign map and must
take a " paper flat " for lack of anything else. Then
it must be folded, and neatly, or it will be like that
morning paper which everyone else has read first—all
projecting corners and lost folds. If it is a smallish
map, place it on the table face down. Fold one half
(say the western) back (with its face up). Get the
edges to fit and ease back to the centre fold line. Then
draw a ruler or the handle of a pocket knife down the
fold. Now turn the western half (of the western half)
back to fit the centre fold, ease back and smooth down
as before. Treat the other half of the map in the
same way. Now the map completely folded from east
to west (and with the map inside) must be folded in
four or six from north to south. Be increasingly careful
as the paper to fold multiplies in thicknesses, and end
off by real pressure. It is a terrible moment when the
trousers emerge from the press with an entirely unsolicited additional crease. It is just as bad with a
map.

A very great thought was the " Ansell " fold. Invented and patented before the Great War, it only
came into its own during its progress. The patent has
lapsed and the idea is enormously useful for those who
use a map " the night before ". So much can be got
on to one piece of paper. The Ordnance Survey have
two maps folded in this way; the 10-mile (road edition
or fully coloured) for the whole of Great Britain, and
a 3-inch of London. Think of covering the whole of
Great Britain on the 10-mile in one sheet, or of using
no more than four $\frac{1}{4}$-inch from Land's End to John o'
Groats! It is done by mounting on both sides, so that
one can pursue one's way always keeping well in the
centre of the map. It is done after this fashion.

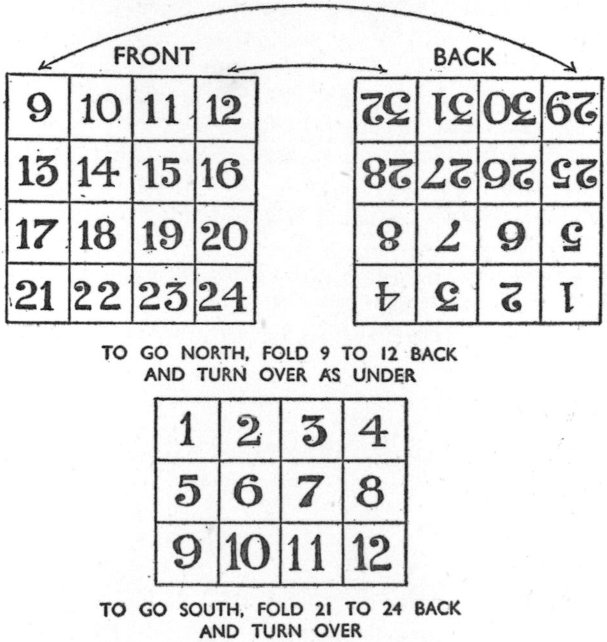
FRONT
BACK
9 10 11 12
13 14 15 16
17 18 19 20
21 22 23 24
32 31 30 29
28 27 26 25
8 7 6 5
4 3 2 1
TO GO NORTH, FOLD 9 TO 12 BACK
AND TURN OVER AS UNDER
1 2 3 4
5 6 7 8
9 10 11 12
TO GO SOUTH, FOLD 21 TO 24 BACK
AND TURN OVER

Fig. 14.—The "Ansell" Fold

I have a $\frac{1}{4}$-inch for the whole of Scotland. It cost about a guinea to make up and it was held to be too much of a luxury article to pay. What is a guinea for all Scotland! Try a similar diagram on a piece of paper and see how it works. It will answer, of course, east and west as easily as north and south.

USEFUL INDEXES TO MAPS, PLANS AND CHARTS

THE PLANS: *England and Wales.*

1. Half-inch Administrative County Diagram. Gives the sheet lines and numbers of sheet for each county

and also all administrative and county boundaries. A valuable index. Price 4s. 6d. (uncoloured, 1s. 6d.)

See also a special half-inch administrative map of the London Traffic Area. A most useful index to all the boundaries of greater London.

2. Half-inch Parish Diagram. Sheet lines, numbers of sheets, and parish boundaries. 2s. 6d.

3. Quarter-inch Civil Parish Diagram (6d.). A reduction of 2.

4. Quarter-inch Petty Sessional Diagram. As in 3, but areas of Summary Jurisdiction and Boroughs which are Local Authorities under Diseases of Animals Act.

Scotland.

An index published in book form to cover the whole country. Price 5s.

MAPS: *Ordnance Survey.*

Probably the indexes of the back of map covers will cover all requirements. If not, separate indexes can be obtained, through agents, for any scale, and edition of the scale.

An excellent pamphlet, "A Description of the Ordnance Survey Small Scale Maps" (now in its 8th edition) can be bought for 1s.

CHAPTER XIII

The 1/M Family

IN Chapter VI the birth of the 1/M map was alluded
to. Growth has been disappointingly slow, and yet,
for all that, there are now some 323 sheets, the majority
of which, however, are labelled provisional and do not
conform, strictly, to international agreement.

Professor Penck of Germany was the first to make
a definite suggestion for the map, and the scale, at an
International Geographical Congress at Berne in 1891.
Resolutions of congresses have small effect, however,
in matters of such wide mapping importance unless
they are adopted and put into effect by government
departments. In most countries they alone have the
means to embark upon so large an enterprise, although
the 1/M international has profited very much from the
energetic co-operation of the British and American
Geographical Societies.

In 1908 at Geneva the International Geographical
Congress was again in session, and a small number of
distinguished geographers determined to take action.
Sir Charles Close, later to be Director General of the
Ordnance Survey, was the moving spirit, and at his
suggestion the British Government invited certain
countries to send delegates to a conference to draw up
a scheme for the sheet lines and conventions of an
international 1/M map. This conference met in London
in 1909.

A further Conference met in Paris in 1913, and since
that date several other 1/M Map Conferences have

been held in connexion with the periodical meetings of the International Geographical Union. The two most important have been those in connexion with the 1928 meeting at Cambridge and the 1934 meeting at Warsaw. The sheets themselves embrace 6° of longitude by 4° of latitude. The map surface, neglecting margins, is thus about 26 × 17 inches near the equator, but naturally becomes smaller as the meridians converge to the poles. In British latitudes the map becomes about 16 × 17 inches. At latitudes of over 60° (north and south) two sheets may be merged into one. The projection is a modification of the polyconic (see Chapter IV), and although each sheet fits its neighbours on its four margins, no more than five (in the form of a cross) can be put together. Contours are generally in brown although the Paris Conference agreed upon black. Black is, however, a bad colour for contours, because it is that of the detail plate on which come so many things that must be altered from time to time. In practice few obeyed the Paris rule and a later conference reverted to the brown colour so universally in use for this purpose. The conventions are good and need no explanation here since they are given on each sheet.

The layer system is probably the best which could be devised, but since it is of necessity world wide in application special cases suffer. Thus the colours are too dark in the case of a really high-lying country such as the high veld of South Africa, and too light for a low-lying country such as Egypt. Sheets are produced by those countries which have the largest amount of territory in the area concerned. Thus France produced the Paris sheet which includes Kent, and Great Britain the London sheet, which includes so much of Normandy and Brittany as to make the French area almost as big as the British. Each country lays down the spelling of every place name within its own borders. Now that so many sheets have appeared it is beginning to be possible to make national sheets from them in exactly the same way as district sheets of the 1-inch followed the completion of the regular series. The Ordnance 1/M of Great Britain in two sheets is but the result of joining up the appropriate parts of seven international sheets. The more this principle is followed the better will other sheets of the same style be understood and used. International sheets are numbered and lettered as follows. Each strip of 4° of latitude from the equator to the pole is given a letter, starting with A for the strip nearest the equator. Each zone of longitude (6°) has its number, starting with that immediately east of the antimeridian of Greenwich (through the Pacific). To complete a reference N. or S. is added according as the sheet is north or south of the equator. Thus the London sheet is N. M-30. Each sheet has its name (not always settled without heartburnings).

The Ordnance Survey Library is the international office and the Ordnance Survey issues annual reports. The greatest drawback to progress lies in the impossibility of fixing a definite price to apply to all sheets. Costs of production vary enormously; and so, alas, does the cartography. Messrs. Stanford & Co. of London are the English agents. This international series is of more use, perhaps, to a geographical student than to the normal man, but none the less the maps are often of the greatest use to travellers. Perhaps the most valuable service it has rendered has been to start all sorts of other national and international mapping enterprise on this scale.

British 1/M's.

This new scale had hardly been introduced in Great Britain when there arose a call for a physical edition (one showing hill features, lakes, rivers, streams and all water, and some topographical names). This is produced in two sheets and is a very good map, although personally I think the best is that on the 10-mile scale.

The next to appear was the map of Roman Britain. So popular is this map that it is now in its third edition. It is the most authoritative record of Roman times in map form; and has resulted in an international series which will be described later. Next came another " period " map of seventeenth-century England, showing the country, the roads, the divisions, and the battles of Cromwell's times. To complete mention of these period maps there has just appeared the southern sheet of a map of " Britain in the Dark Ages ", a picture of the state of the country in the epoch A.D. 410 to A.D. 871, which covers our history between the departure of the Romans and the crowning of King Alfred. These period maps are admirably got up and include, within their covers, exceedingly interesting notes by well-known experts. They are well worth a place on the map shelf.

A population map in two sheets illustrates the 1931 census. The presentation is as clear as it is interesting. Population is " contoured " and then layer coloured. There are some who refer to these population contours as "isopleths". To invent these doubtful Greek words with the aid of a lexicon must be great fun, but is unfair to those who either never had one or who have long since disposed of it to a son, or to the best advantage.

The Geological Survey has a 1/M of the coal-fields, and is about to publish a complete 1/M Geological, which will greatly add to the importance of this 1/M family. It is, indeed, quite evident that we shall see a great development, largely on this scale, of the illustration of matters of national interest. The main difficulty of historical mapping is to provide a correct picture of the country, its roads, its forests, even its coast-line, at the period in question. If it can be done at all it is, however, obvious that it is far better and more convincingly done on a map than in words. For any industrial or sociological analysis the background of to-day is ready to hand.

International derivatives of the 1/M.

It is odd that Great Britain, on the farthest outpost line of the Roman Empire, should have started an international series of maps to show its organisation and development. It is entirely owing to the interest and energy of Mr. O. G. S. Crawford, the Ordnance Survey Archæological Officer, and the author of all its period maps, that this plan was proposed, accepted and put into execution. The general idea of the series of fifty-one sheets is well summed up in the following paragraphs taken from official reports:

" The principal object of the Commission is to produce a map of the Roman Empire which will be of use both to students and to the general public. The Commission regards it as most important therefore to keep the map *as clear and simple as possible*. It should be borne in mind that it is to be a historical map, not an archæological one. It is not designed to serve as a guide or index map of ancient monuments, but to show the distribution and character of population, the names of towns and natural features, the economic and social conditions of the period. For this reason monuments, in themselves of considerable archæological interest, such as amphitheatres, are to be omitted, since they always occur immediately outside towns which are marked on the map. Only cities that were actually inhabited during the Roman period or during some portion of it, will be shown. Only remains (visible or destroyed) of the Roman period will be shown. No prehistoric remains will be shown.

" The undermentioned countries have participated in the scheme: Great Britain, Italy, France, Spain, Germany, Egypt, Austria, Switzerland."

The 1/M seems a very small scale to us in England,

yet it is, oddly enough, too large for some of the many unsurveyed areas of the world which constitute some sixty per cent of its surface. Partly for that reason the British, French and Belgian mapping offices concerned in the outside world (in our case the Geographical Section of the General Staff, or M.I. 4) have collaborated in a 1/2M of Africa. This is an admirable series and the British area is extremely well layered to show heights. Any traveller in the Africa of Negroes and Bantus (not the northern fringe) will do well to get the sheets which cover his route. The sheets are on the same projection and have much the same conventions as the 1/M. The habit of working on the 1/M projection and sheet lines is spreading. The new French 1/500,000 is another example.

One can imagine the atlas of the League of Nations of the future equipped with sheets depicting the population densities, speeches, religions, occupations, communications, raw materials, and defence organizations of its constituent parts. How many speeches would they spare!

Other interesting Maps.

The best general map of Asia for the comprehensive idea is the 1/4M of Asia produced by the Geographical Section of the General Staff. It is beautifully drawn, contoured, and layered, includes Russia and Asia Minor and curiously enough Abyssinia (in the South Arabian sheet). Abyssinia is therefore available both in this series and in the 1/2M of Africa. But the 1/4M is big enough to show as much as one can swear to of Abyssinia. This series is on the Lambert conical orthomorphic with two standard parallels (see page 42) and the scale suffers a bit in the extreme south, but for anyone interested generally in the Near East, India, China, or Japan its sheets are the greatest help.

Those who are interested in prehistoric times will value " Neolithic Wessex ", one of the ¼-inch sheets which record a survey presently to appear, we are told, on a 1/M edition. Several other sheets of this survey are available.

Those interested in agriculture and in land utilization will find the *Agricultural Atlas* (it costs 10s.) the most authoritative guide, whilst a special edition of the " popular edition " of the 1-inch is being used by Professor Dudley Stamp as the background for a land utilization map.

Finally, those who wish to study the population densities of the area of greater London (corresponding to the London Traffic Area) can buy an excellent half-inch, illustrating the 1931 census figures for that area.

Messrs. Stanford Ltd. of 12/14 Long Acre, and of 43 Whitehall, have all these maps and the indexes and particulars relating to them.

CHAPTER XIV

Geological Maps

GEOLOGY was the first of all sciences to start mapping itself, and to do so has either had to make use of whatever maps existed (as the indispensable background) or else to settle down to map the country first and its geology afterwards. The first geological map of Great Britain (England and Wales) was produced in 1815 by William Smith. This was, however, before the days of an official survey. The Ordnance Survey formed an " Ordnance Geological Survey " in 1832, with De la Beche in England and Portlock in Ireland. The geological survey followed closely on the progress of the mapping, and was much used, in those early days, by the hill sketchers who prepared the models for the hachuring.

In 1840 De la Beche asked that the 6-inch plans of the South Wales coal-fields should be contoured in order to help his geological survey, a fact which had much to do with our subsequent policy. In 1854 the Geological Survey was transferred from the Board of Ordnance to the newly formed Department of Science and Art, which was then under the Board of Trade, and subsequently (from 1856 onwards) came under the Board of Education. In 1919 the Geological Survey was transferred to the Department of Scientific and Industrial Research and has recently moved to a fine new building in Exhibition Road.

The " general " geological map is at the scale of 25 miles to the inch, and an admirable map too. It is,

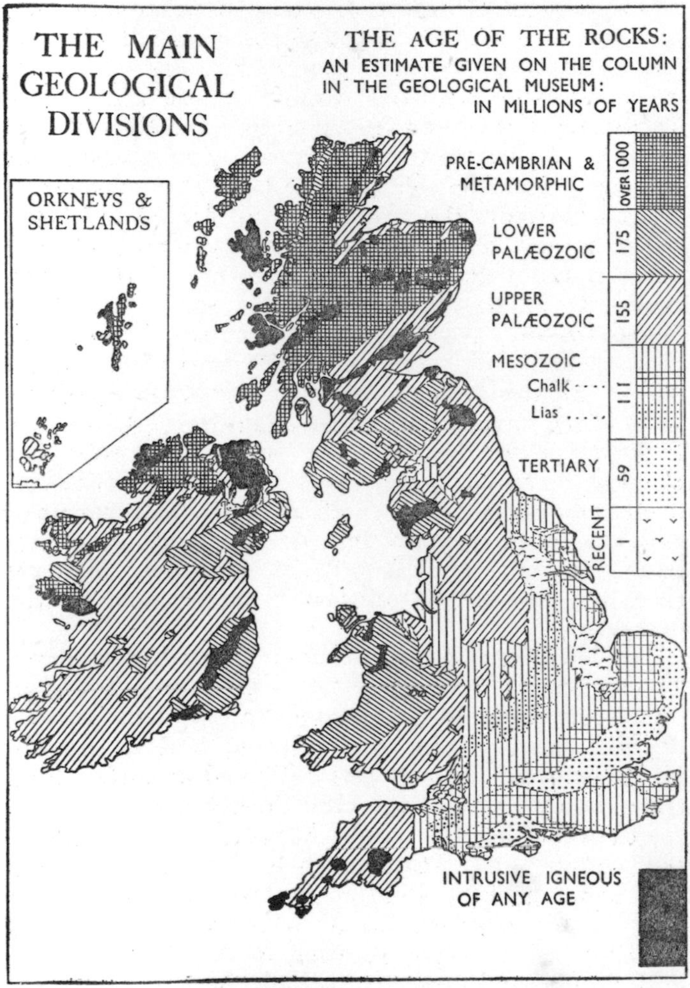
THE MAIN GEOLOGICAL DIVISIONS
THE AGE OF THE ROCKS:
AN ESTIMATE GIVEN ON THE COLUMN IN THE GEOLOGICAL MUSEUM:
IN MILLIONS OF YEARS
ORKNEYS & SHETLANDS
PRE-CAMBRIAN & METAMORPHIC
OVER 1000
LOWER PALÆOZOIC
175
UPPER PALÆOZOIC
155
MESOZOIC
Chalk
Lias
111
TERTIARY
59
RECENT
1
INTRUSIVE IGNEOUS OF ANY AGE

Fig. 15.—The Structure of Great Britain

however, good news that there is soon to be a new
1/M Geological. There are lots of maps now on the 1/M,
and two of them, the physical (showing hill features,
rivers and all water, and some names) and the population (showing the 1931 census), are so much more
interesting if they can be compared directly with the
geology. An excellent general map, now, it seems, out
of print, was a 10-mile produced by Bartholomew in
1892, made under the direction of Sir Archibald Geikie.

The earliest made and most widely used geological
series is the 1-inch. The first edition of the 1-inch
geological of England and Wales was based upon
Mudge's map (the old series and mainly the result of
compass and chain surveys at 2, 3, or 6 inches to the
mile). All the geology was engraved upon a copperplate which already carried the map itself. As in other
geological series there are two editions, the solid and
the drift. The latter deals with those surface displace-
ments and deposits due to glacial drift. The sheets of
this old series, printed from copper and (generally)
hand coloured, were often fairly expensive. Many of
them are now out of print as being replaced by the
new series.

The New Series 1-inch is colour printed from stone.
The sequence of its preparation is given on p. 199 as an
interesting example of the co-operation of the various
drawing, photographic and printing trades. As will
be remembered the new series differed in outline from
the old only south of the Hull-Preston line (see p. 72).
North of that line the numbering of the sheets changed,
but nothing else. Consequently the old series and
new series geological differ in those northern parts
only in the substitution of lithography for copper
printing and of colour printing for hand colouring.

Both old and new series had sheet memoirs ex-
planatory of the geology, but often enough one memoir
serves both editions.

In Scotland there was no difference of outline between first and second editions of the normal 1-inch. As stated in Chapter VI they were plotted on a different projection to England and were larger sheets. The geological editions differ, however, just as they do in England and consist of an earlier, printed from copper and hand coloured, and a later, colour printed and on stone. The new edition is, as yet, far from complete. If anyone is really interested in colour printing, as well as in a singularly tortured geology, let him buy for 3s. the 1923 solid and drift geological map (sheet 44) of Mull. As in England sheets have their separate memoirs and there are many published sections both horizontal and vertical.

The ¼-inch geological is based upon that old ¼-inch ordnance map " with its known imperfections " referred to in Chapter VI. The first edition is now completely out of print. The second, covering Great Britain, but with the old break of projection at the Border, is colour printed from stone. Its preparation is very like that of the later 1-inch. There are no actual quarter-sheet memoirs, but there are a lot of district memoirs, as well as the new series of eighteen handbooks on " British Regional Geology ", and these are often better illustrated by the ¼-inch than by the 1-inch.

The 6-inch geological covers coal-fields and areas of peculiar importance, but is far from being general. It is printed on the latest 6-inch revision available at the date of its geological survey, and is a black and blue map, for the geology is over printed in blue, and then hand coloured if desired. An exception to the general rule is the 6-inch of London (referred to on p. 4) which is colour printed.

Roughly speaking the colour printed geological 1-inch costs 2s. in England and Wales, and 3s. for the larger Scottish sheet.

The ¼-inch costs 3s. a sheet.

The 6-inch uncoloured, but geology in blue, 2s. 3d., whilst if it is to be hand coloured the punishment is made to fit the crime. Obviously a Norfolk sheet with simple geology will cost less than one of a mineralized district of complex structure.

Almost all geological maps are sold flat and unmounted.

The Geological Survey produces so much technical matter that the " List of memoirs, maps, sections, &c.", published at 1s. and brought up to date on the 31st December, 1933, should be in the possession of any who are interested geologically in a large area. There is also a useful uncoloured edition of the 25-mile, with the 1-inch and ¼-inch indexes overprinted in front and the list of memoirs and sections behind.

As regards colours and conventional signs the Geological Survey follows the admirable rule of making each sheet self-explanatory. The 1-inch (colour printed) has its colour scheme and its multitude of signs and conventions printed in the east and west margins, whilst a vertical section often occupies part of the southern margin. No general index to 1-inch colours and conventions exists, and indeed it would be a formidable task to compile one. The ¼-inch presents less difficulty and there is a fairly comprehensive guide to its colours and conventions sold separately.

Geological maps are printed by the Ordnance Survey and on sale at Ordnance Survey agents, where indexes and lists may be seen.

Those who wish to pursue the subject as interested, rather than professional, students may well read one or other (or all) of the following books:

S. T. Shand, *Earth Lore*, 1933, Thomas Murby & Co. 5s.

S. T. Shand, *Useful Aspects of Geology*, 1934, Thomas Murby & Co. 6s.

Arthur R. Dwerryhouse, *Geological and Topographical Maps—Their Interpretation and Use*, 1919, Edward Arnold. 6s.

But anyone really interested should visit the New Geological Museum in Exhibition Road. On the ground floor are bays arranged to illustrate the geology of the various "regions", which are explained at length in the Handbooks of Regional Geology (referred to above). Dioramas, maps, models, and photographs are all called in to assist.

CHAPTER XV

The Weather Map

THE map of "To-day's Weather" in the morning paper gives more figure and sign, and less outline, than is common on a map. It is more explanation than delineation; resembles a chart more than a map, but is known, indifferently, as either. The morning paper generally adds a full explanation of the symbols used upon its chart. It may, none the less, be a help to give the explanation again, because there is so much to absorb in the paper before the work of the day begins that it is as well to learn it once for all.

Let me start by saying that the right thing to do really is to procure a copy of that admirable pamphlet *The Weather Map—an Introduction to Modern Meteorology* (H.M. Stationery Office, 3s.). What follows here is the barest outline.

Forecasting is naturally dependent upon that international co-operation which is so arranged as to collect information over a wide area and upon a uniform plan. An airman might well eat every meal of the day in a different country, and weather, nearly as fast moving, would be upon us without possible forewarning, were it not for the 700 or so co-operating observing stations, reinforced by frequent reports from ships. Reports from observing stations are exchanged at stated hours, so as to give the forecasters of each nation a reasonable chance of following a definite programme and time-table. The task of forecasting thus includes the collection of facts and measurements relating to a period

already passed (though these include " tendencies "
of various sorts), and then the interesting task of
prophesying in what way the situation so disclosed
will develop over Great Britain. The biggest gap in
measurement is that in the air itself. Winds, pressures,
temperatures, rainfall and, in fact, weather are all
affected by the rise and fall of the land, its woods and
forests, and even its cities and individual buildings.
A little way up (say, 3000 feet) conditions are much
less influenced by the peculiarities of the surface and
give a much firmer indication of probability. Some
day, no doubt, that gap will be filled. Meanwhile,
forecasting, rapidly gaining in accuracy, must still rest
largely on the evidence of past happenings. Such and
such a movement over the Atlantic, with such and such
pressures and temperatures, resulted in a weather for
East Anglia, which may very probably repeat itself
under the same conditions (say) ten years later.

Pressure is measured by the barometer. Unfortunately we have to get into foreign units to follow
the weather map. Normally in England pressure is
read in so many inches of mercury. The weight of
air supports a column of mercury some 30 inches
high on the average. But in forecasting we must needs
measure internationally and the unit chosen is the
millibar. One millibar is the pressure exerted by 1000
dynes per square centimetre, a definition which will
leave most of us cold. However, 1000 millibars is
roughly " one atmosphere ", and equals about 29·53
inches of mercury or 14·7 lb. per square inch. Normally
speaking, then, the tires of one's car want 2000 millibars
to be comfortable (although abroad it is advisable to
ask for 2 atmospheres as more generally understood!).

Lines of equal pressure, or pressure contours, are
known to the learned as isobars. The " vertical interval " is generally 4 millibars, and corresponds to
$\frac{1}{8}$ of an inch of mercury. Gradients are often talked of,
and are, in idea, for pressure exactly as they are for

height, that is, the vertical interval divided by the horizontal equivalent (see p. 29). The vertical interval is the rise or fall of pressure in millibars between two pressure contours. The horizontal equivalent is the distance between, and perpendicular to, them (the steepest slope). These pressure contours surround both elevations (anticyclones) and depressions (or cyclones) and it would help a little if they were given in some different form of line (say dotted for the decreasing pressure contours of a depression). The centres of depressions and anticyclones are however marked " Low " and " High " respectively. Daily papers' weather charts give the appropriate pressures in the margin opposite the pressure contours.

Winds are shown by arrows with varying numbers of feathers upon them. It was Admiral Sir Francis Beaufort, K.C.B., D.C.L., F.R.S., hydrographer from 1820 to 1855, who was responsible for their design, and for the letters which appear on maps as descriptive of the weather generally. Beaufort was shipwrecked, and later nearly drowned, early in his service, and whilst hydrographer had parties at work all over the world. It is little wonder that he was interested in meteorology, but perhaps singular that he was also interested in antiquities, and had much in common in this respect with Generals Roy and Colby who had so much to do with mapping and the Ordnance Survey. Beaufort's arrows are to be redesigned for 1936. It will be as well to show the new model and not the old. The new differs indeed only by giving half a feather for each of Beaufort's whole feathers. International weather symbols are given as well as Beaufort's letter abbreviations.

A wind naturally tends to blow straight ahead along the line in which it is moving. If it is bent it has the same tendency (on the bend) to fly off at a tangent as do drops of water on a rotating mop head. But it also tends (in the northern hemisphere) to turn to the right (looking from feather to point of the arrow) because of the earth's rotation, and finally it tends to carry out its original purpose which is to equalize pressure, and to carry air from the denser to the shallower areas. The result of these mutually disturbing influences is that winds round a depression (in the northern hemisphere) move anticlockwise and are generally edging inwards towards the centre. Round an anticyclone the winds are clockwise and tend (if anything) to point outwards, but in general they are much lighter than those round a depression. The morning paper generally adds the velocity of the wind in miles per hour within small circles on the arrows themselves.

I wonder whether the B.B.C. announcer leaves all of us the wiser when he tells us that the wind will be *veering slightly and backing later*. A wind is called after the point of the compass from which it blows. Thus an east wind is, all too obviously, a wind from the east. We like it to veer, which it does by shifting clockwise to east-south-east, south-east, south, and so on. On the other hand, if it backs, it shifts counterclockwise to east-north-east, north-east, and so on. But be careful if you go for a cruise in a sailing ship, or if you settle down to enjoy *Midshipman Easy*. The Ancient Mariner (in sail) used to say, and still does, that a wind " veers " when it shifts aft, and " hauls " when it shifts forward.

A depression may be pictured as a very large, flat, slowly rotating anticlockwise whirlpool which forms at the boundary between two masses of air of different origin. If the two masses of air are derived from polar and tropical regions respectively the former will be cold and dense and the latter warm and light.

The main boundary between air from arctic regions and air from equatorial regions is called the Polar Front. The air to the north of the Polar Front is cold and moves to the west, while the air to the south is

warm and moves to the east. When undisturbed the
Polar Front runs due east and west, but when a dis-
turbance forms it becomes distorted. The whirling
motion set up does not destroy the junction between
the two air masses but produces a large northward
indentation in the boundary. On the west side of this
bay or indentation the cold air cuts under the warm
air and pushes it upwards; this is called the "cold
front"; while on the other side of the bay the warm
air rises up over the cold air as though it were mounting
a wedge; this is called the "warm front". The bay
itself which is composed of warm air is called the
"warm sector". The air which rises at the warm
front cools and causes overcast skies and steady rain,
while the warm air which is violently lifted up at the
cold front gives rise to towering clouds and heavy
showers, often developing into thunderstorms. As a
depression approaches from the west one sees at first
thin cloud high up in the sky. This is cloud which has
formed in the stream of warm air rising over the wedge
of cold air, the thin end of which is many miles to the
west where the "warm front" lies. As the depression
comes still nearer, the cloud gets thicker and lower until
when the warm front is only a short distance away
there is low cloud and steady rain.

With the passage of the warm front the warm segment is entered, the rain ceases and there is a slight
rise of temperature. The sky generally remains clouded,
with slight intermittent rain in the warm segment.
The passage of the cold front is accompanied by heavy
showers, a rise in the barometer and a shift of the
wind from south-west or west to north-west. As soon
as the cold front passes blue sky appears between the
showers and the weather clears with cold fresh air
until the next depression approaches.

A worse enemy, however, is the secondary. He,
more malignant than his parent, revolves generally in
the same anticlockwise direction round the main

depression, but is often associated with heavier rain and fiercer winds. A "secondary" almost always causes a heavy downpour.

But an anticyclone, especially in winter, is generally associated with an "inverted temperature gradient". That is, the air cools with height up to a definite level and then begins to warm up again for a bit. Warm air from below cannot rise through it and has no chance to cool off and discharge its watery content. An anticyclone may be, and in summer generally is, associated with a clear sunny sky, but in winter and spring, is just as often associated with fog, cloudy skies and cold. The blanket (where the temperature gradient begins to invert) collects cloud, and may add soot and dirt to its collection. Moreover, the light winds of an anticyclone do not help to clear away these winter and spring troubles. The anticyclone may be a summer joy, but it may do damage to garden and orchard in the spring and Buchan's cold periods are its consequences.

In order to illustrate anticyclone, depression, secondary depression, and the conventions of a weather chart, fig. 16 has been added. To the best of my knowledge no such combination of weather has ever afflicted Great Britain. The secondary depression lies to the south of the main depression. To the north-east (where "Barometer falling" is written) there is a Col,[1] so called on topographical analogy, in the ridge of high pressure running north and south. To either side of the col are the depression "deeps". A "V-shaped depression" is not shown, but does occur sometimes, and the winds at the point of the V are known as discontinuous because of the sharp reversal of direction. It will be noticed that this figure follows a common custom of omitting the barb of the wind arrow, and of giving instead a circle, within which is the strength of the wind in miles per hour. Near that circle the temperature, in degrees Fahrenheit, is also given.

[1] A neck, saddle, or ridge of land connecting two mountains or hills.

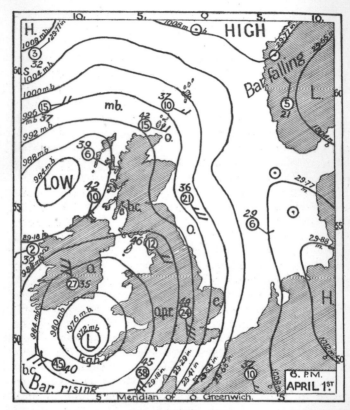

Fig. 16.—Weather Chart

Pressure is given both in millibars and in inches of mercury.

The charts in the papers are, generally, to a scale of about 1/30,000,000. Weather maps prepared and exhibited at the Air Ministry are known as the 7-hour (7 a.m.) and 13-hour (1 p.m.) maps and the forecasts shown refer to the remainder of the current day in both cases. Press forecasts in the morning papers depend upon a 13-hour (1 p.m.) or 18-hour (6 p.m.)

Beaufort No.	Wind	Arrow	Speed m.p.h.	Commonly observed Effects of Corresponding Winds
0	Calm		0	Calm, smoke rises vertically.
1	Light air		2	Direction of wind shown by smoke drift, but not by wind vanes.
2	Light breeze		5	Wind felt on face; leaves rustle, ordinary vane moved by wind.
3	Gentle breeze		10	Leaves and small twigs in constant motion; wind extends light flag.
4	Moderate breeze		15	Raises dust and loose paper; small branches are moved.
5	Fresh breeze		21	Small trees in leaf begin to sway, crested wavelets form on inland waters.
6	Strong breeze		27	Large branches in motion ; whistling heard in telephone wires; umbrellas used with difficulty.
7	Moderate gale		35	Whole trees in motion; inconvenience felt in walking against wind.
8	Fresh gale		42	Breaks twigs off trees; generally impedes progress.
9	Strong gale		50	Slight structural damage occurs, (chimney pots and slates removed).
10	Whole gale		59	Seldom experienced inland; trees uprooted; considerable structural damage occurs.
11	Storm		68	Very rarely experienced; accompanied by widespread damage.
12	Hurricane		above 75	

THE BEAUFORT LETTERS AND INTERNATIONAL SYMBOLS

1. Appearance of Sky.

    b   Blue sky whether with clear or hazy atmosphere.
    c   Cloudy, i.e. detached opening clouds.
    o   Overcast, i.e. the whole sky covered with one impervious cloud.
    g   Gloom.
    u   Ugly, threatening sky.

2. Wind.

    q   Squalls.
    KQ   Line squalls.

3. Precipitation.

    r   Rain.
    p   Passing showers.
    d   Drizzle.
    s   Snow.
    rs   Sleet.
    h   Hail.

4. Electrical Phenomena.

    t   Thunder.
    l   Lightning.
    tl   Thunderstorm.

5. Atmospheric Obscurity and Water Vapour.

    f   Fog
    fe   Wet fog } range of visibility less than 1100 yards.
    z   Haze, range of visibility 1100 yards or more, but less than 2200 yards.
    m   Mist, range of visibility 1100 yards or more, but less than 2200 yards.
    v   Unusual visibility of distant objects.
    e   Wet air, without rain falling.
    y   Dry air, with less than 60 per cent humidity.

6. Ground Phenomena.

    w   Dew.
    x   Hoar frost.

chart and refer to the period 6 a.m. to midnight of the following day. Those in the evening papers come from the 7 a.m. chart and refer to the period between noon that day, and noon the next.

Authorities.

The Weather Map. An introduction to modern meteorology. Second edition, 1930 (H.M. Stationery Office, 3*s*.).

Examples of Weather Maps. No. 337. (9 Depression, 18 Anticyclone, 21 Secondary Depression, 22 V-shaped Depression, 23 Wedge, 24 Col.) 3*d*. each (3½*d*. post free). H.M. Stationery Office.

CHAPTER XVI

Helping Oneself

ONE may want to do all sorts of things to one's maps and plans. Many of them can be done quite easily at home. Let us take some of the most obvious matters, which will probably be :

(*a*) Surveying new buildings or roads.

(*b*) Drawing them on the plan, or map.

(*c*) Adding flat washes of colour (for one of many possible reasons).

(*d*) Mounting several maps or plans together on linen.

As an example let us survey a new hospital on to a 6-inch plan, draw it and add its title, add layer tints to show up the contours and slopes, not only on that plan but on five more to cover (in the six) a whole estate, and finally mount all six on linen so as to form a complete map.

(*a*) *The Survey of the Hospital* (see fig. 17).

When Great Britain was unsurveyed, to get this hospital properly mapped would have meant Gunter's chains, several helpers, and a day or two. Now it is but a matter of fitting it into an already completed survey. Let us take a lesson from the sailor. Sailing "coastwise" his navigation is largely a question of getting two points (or navigation marks) in a line. Where two such lines intersect position is certain. This same principle is that followed in the revision of our national plans. It is indeed the principle illustrated in

Chapter X, and holds good wherever existing maps and plans are trustworthy. The illustration given in fig. 17 represents a simple and easy case. That is all to the good, for every case is different. There is no theory worth talking about. Everything depends on getting two already mapped points in line, and using these lines to cut down new measurement to the minimum. It is for that reason that a linen tape will be enough.

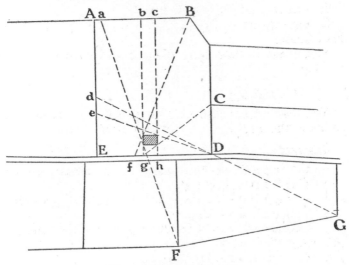

Fig, 17.—Adding detail to a Plan

Problem: To insert new hospital in plan of field ABCDE.

Available: A 6-inch plan on a piece of board, a 2H pencil and indiarubber, a 100-foot linen tape.

Approach by path from north of A.

1. Reaching A, measure along fence AB, till in a line [at (a)] with S.W. corner of house and fence corner F. Draw ray.

2. Measuring on along AB, reach (b) and then (c), where lines of sides of house cut AB, mark points (b)

and (c) with strips of the morning *Times* and plot them on the plan.

3. Walking on down AE stop where line GD cuts fence—mark it on plan. Measure down to (e), so that (e)D cuts N.E. corner of house. Draw ray.

4. Cross stile at E. Measure from E to (f) where (f)B touches N.W. corner of house. Draw ray.

5. Measure on to (g) so that (g)(b) touches W. of house. Draw ray. Observe at (g) that (g)C touches S.E. corner of house. Draw ray.

6. Measure on to (h) such that (h)(c) is in line with E of house.

The house is now fully defined and with sufficient check.

(b) *The Drawing*.

Now having got the plan in pencil the problem is to make the additions neatly and permanently.

Required.

1. A " ruling " or " drawing " pen (usually called " drawing " in catalogues).

2. A " card " of " Ladies' " or " Crowquill " pen-nibs.

3. A good straight edge.

4. A boxwood scale of feet, at 6 inches to the mile (in this particular case).

5. Two set squares, 45° and 60°.

6. A gauge for the size of letter in writing names.

7. A piece of transfer paper.

8. A bottle of black waterproof ink.[1]

Let us examine these. A ruling pen is a good thing to have about the house. It has a straight handle, ending off in two blades, the tips of which converge holding between them the waterproof ink. The size of line it draws is controlled by a screw which opens or closes the blades. If none is available use a ladies'

[1] The best British variety is Black " Progress " from Drawing Office Supplies Ltd., 51 Cheapside, E.C.2.

nib. But a nib is inky, whereas a ruling pen keeps the ink inside. If you must use a nib turn the straight edge over so that the bevelled edge is well off the paper and not flat on it. Otherwise ink from the nib finds its way on to the plan by way of the straight edge. For to draw a straight line one must draw along a straight edge.

Is the latter worthy of its name? Draw a pencil line with its aid, keeping the pencil always at the same angle. (Even that requires practice.) Turn the straight edge end for end, and putting it on the farther side of the line draw along it. Do line and edge coincide? If not either you or the straight edge is at fault.

The boxwood scale should be graduated in feet.

The set squares not only give the necessary right angles but also parallel lines. Having set one edge of a set square along a line, and placed the second against the edge perpendicular, the first can be slid up and down for parallel lines.

A gauge is the usefullest thing and absurdly easy to make. For example, if it is desired to add a road of a general width of 14 feet, then a slip of wood cut down to the required width (to scale!), and with two pins lashed on each side, will trace two parallel lines through a piece of transfer paper. A small " bowsweep " compass (you will find it in all catalogues) acts admirably as a gauge because the points can be set at any distance apart, and can be used therefore at any " gauge ". Do not use typewriting carbon transfer paper as it marks a greasy line difficult to rub out. Tissue paper rubbed with Nixey's black lead makes a good transfer paper, but even a B pencil (otherwise taboo for surveying) rubbed well over a piece of thin writing paper will do.

The hospital will have some title or other. It should be written in the normal type for such an institution (see the margin), and, to make a job of it, neatly. Gauge the size. Draw the parallel lines in pencil. Lay off the correct widths of the letters (experts do

all these things, so why not you?)   Pencil in lightly.
See that the spacing is right, that the slope of each
letter is correct and that each one touches the top
and the bottom line.   Then with waterproof black ink,
a ladies' nib, and courage, start away.   The time of
preparation is over now, however.   Firm strokes, please,
and no pen-painting.

The outlines of new buildings, roads, spinneys,
perhaps, will have been done in pencil.   A 2H is amply
soft enough, and should be kept as sharp as a needle.
The " striking " strip of an old match box will keep
it so. See that every house is drawn rectangular (which
is generally the case in this country).   Then pen in.
Perhaps you wish to " hatch " the house (i.e. to fill in
the plan of it with thin parallel lines).   If so, be sure to
make them parallel, for nothing looks worse than
irregularly spaced and sloped hatching.   Keep the same
width and same angle of hatching for all that you add
throughout the plan.   It is a good thing to try out your
pen on an odd bit of paper before every new item.
There seems to be a multitude of superfluous hairs in
this world.   If there is a blot, or a line drawn too far,
the offence must be erased. Be careful never to use the
point of a knife.   Rub smoothly and evenly with part
of the cutting edge, then use the indiarubber, and
finally smooth down the erased portion with a bit of
bone if there is one handy. (The handle of a table knife
will serve.)   The final rubbing restores the surface to
some extent.   Draughtsmen usually keep a highly
treasured shark's tooth for the purpose.   No paper is
the better for being rubbed and cleaned.   Moreover,
subsequent washes of colour are more difficult to add
neatly, for the injured fibres collect the grit which is
generally present in the " wash ".   In the drawing and
penning in stages it is best to rest the hand on paper
(or tracing paper) and not on the plan itself.   If by
any chances you draw on, or add colour to, tracing
paper it is advisable to go over the whole surface first

with indiarubber. The surface is a little greasy and is much improved by a preliminary rub.

(c) Colour Washes.

The next job is to make a succession of layer tints to show up the lie of the land. In choosing a scheme of layer colours, avoid mixing different colours. This is no coat for Joseph, but a map with many things to show. To turn it into a rainbow will spoil it. A light cream (chrome yellow and white) for the lowest, followed by gradually deepening buffs and browns as height increases will serve the purpose best. The best watercolour paints to use are the hard or cake variety, mixed by rubbing in a saucer. Finish off by rubbing the mixed colour with a smooth cork in order to break up all the particles. The layer may be between contours which twist about a bit, and include a largish area. A flat wash is the only way to do it, and repeated appeals to the cake of paint itself will certainly destroy the flatness. Mix a good saucerful of the colour you are going to start on and let the grit sink to the bottom of the saucer. A water-colour or sable brush (about size 7), or goose brush, will be best. Before starting to colour, rub over the surface with a damp sponge (not too wet) in order to remove dust, and possibly a fingermark or two. If the map is well worn, and the surface greasy, rub it over with ox gall. In using the brush do not put the point in the saucer, but bring the hairs to a point all the same. Let the side of the brush lie on the surface of the colour and turn it round till the brush has lots in it. Once started, let nothing interrupt you, or calamity waits! It is a help to have the plan on a slight slope, so that gravity helps the brush to keep a " wet edge ". If that is allowed to dry an entirely unsolicited line will appear in the flat wash.

If there is an awkward shape to follow with the brush, keep dabbing the wet edge a little bit farther on, as you follow the pattern. When the end is reached there will be the now unnecessary wet edge to get rid of. Dry the brush in blotting paper and let it suck up the last moisture. Once done, the brush can be dropped and the other calls of life (such as the telephone) attended to.

(d) Mounting.

The most difficult of all these minor jobs is to mount maps together. No doubt the most usual case is to join two individual sheets, and it may be that the maps in question are " paper flat " copies. Supposing the two sheets are north and south of each other respectively. The easiest way is to cut the title and top margin off the southern sheet and use the lower margin of the northern sheet for the paste. To cut off the top margin use a really sharp knife. It is almost impossible to cut an accurate line with scissors. An old safety-razor blade fitted between two " Mecanno " strips of about four inches in length makes an excellent cutter. A bit of zinc or glass with a sheet of paper round it will be found convenient to cut upon, and the straightedge will be wanted to guide the knife. Then comes the trouble of fit. Paper is very tiresome with its contractions and expansions. It is unlikely that the two *will* fit exactly. You may then expand the shorter one by damping it (having laid it map downwards on the table) or you may contract the larger by warming it. That is done by holding it near a gas-ring or hot plate. Both expansion and contraction may be necessary. For this easiest case a bottle of " Gloy " will be a good enough adhesive. Put it on sparingly, spread it evenly, and wait till the gloy is " tacky " as it dries. Finally fit the southern map into its place. Get the centre point correct and ease the rest down gently. If a " pucker " or " bubble " forms, lift it up again as far back as the trouble and then smooth down with the hand with a bit of thin paper between the hand and the map. Never try to smooth a bubble out until you have allowed the air to escape!

A much more interesting case is that of the set, previously mentioned, of six 6-inch sheets to be mounted together on linen. The linen to get is nainsook, or any other light close woven linen. For six 6-inch sheets (i.e. three north and south and two east and west) we shall want 38 inches by 38 inches (allowing 1 inch for a margin all round). It is easiest to mount on linen with the problem in front of you on an easel or stand. Perhaps the garage door would do, perhaps there is a blackboard handy. If not, a kitchen table seems indicated. The linen should be pinned dry on the board, stretching it as the pinning goes on. The next item is the paste. There are three possibilities:

1. Gloy. (It will use a lot! and gloy is not the best.)

2. Rex Paste Powder. Mix cold—about a teacupful to a quart of water—stir well. (You can buy this powder at any paperhanger's).

3. Ordinary flour paste.

Of these number 2 is the best. The paste brush may be anything large enough, which is clean. A small distemper brush, or a large paint brush will serve.

Whilst the paste is making, cut the sheets. There is a word of wisdom to come here. To "butt" two sheets cut to a common edge is excessively difficult. It is best to allow a small margin on one side of the join and paste the other down over it. According to expert custom about $\frac{3}{16}$ inch is left as margin to be covered by the next sheet. Numbering the sheets, from the top western corner (one and two being the top row, three and four the second, &c.), then number one would have top and western margin intact, bottom and eastern cut down to $\frac{3}{16}$ inch; whilst number two, retaining its full eastern margin, would be cut flush on the western. When all are cut, paste all the backs of the sheets. A paperhanger ends off by doubling his wallpaper paste to paste, and this can be done with maps too; or else they can be laid back to back (paste to paste). When all are done, sponge over the linen.

Now put number one lightly into place. If it goes on askew you will certainly run off the linen. Fit number two on to number one, and follow successively till all are on. Now go over the joins and fit exactly by pressing this way and that with the fingers. Finally give the whole a rub down with the hand over a piece of thin paper. If the final fit has made a wrinkle or two press them down with a hot iron when dry.

Perhaps you may want to mount an Ansell fold for yourself. This is a problem in " section mounting ", leaving a small portion of linen (between the sections) without covering map. As each section is so far independent that it does not actually " butt " on to others the exact fit is not quite so important. First stretch the nainsook on the board or table. Then draw your scheme of sections on it. Cut the sections to fit. Finally get the paste pot and finish off. You will have to buy " paper flats " from which to cut the sections.

One last problem. Have you some old plans on paper, or tracing paper, to patch? Perhaps the edges are cracking and breaking away. Perhaps a cracked old fold threatens to give. The best repairs are those with " Nadir Tape ", an adhesive transparent paper sold in small rolls. It can be got from the Ozolid Company Ltd., Westminster. Similar transparent mending adhesive is to be obtained, however, from any music dealers.

CHAPTER XVII

The Grand Tour

"Heureux qui, comme Ulysse, a fait un beau voyage."
— *Joachim du Bellay.*

EVERYTHING is comparative. The grandest possible tour in one case might be from London to Brighton, or in another from Glasgow to the Trossachs. This short chapter is devoted, however, to those who go farther afield and who want to study, on a map, the main features—the general lie of the land—in the parts to which they go. Such will probably have bought J. F. Horrobin's *Atlas of Current Affairs* (Victor Gollancz, Ltd., 1934) and acquired an idea of the political background from the admirable sketch maps therein. They will, no doubt, also have Doctor A. C. Haddon's *Wanderings of Peoples* (Cambridge University Press, 1912) and from its sketch maps have identified the various strains which produced the blends of humanity most likely to be met with. The next question is what topographical maps, if any, to buy in advance. The choice is rather a limited one. No one is likely to carry a whole atlas, but most will be anxious to have something, small in bulk and easy to carry, to give the general idea.

In Europe the most convenient answer lies in the two sheets, at 1/3 M, of Western and Eastern Europe, produced by Bartholomew. These are up-to-date,

suitably mounted and folded, and as full of information
as the scale will allow.

Asia is easier, for the War Office series at 1/4M is
admirable. The individual sheets will pay for section
mounting and folding (sections are convenient for the
"general purpose map") since they are usually supplied
flat and without covers. Two of these sheets give an
admirable picture of India with all the frontier regions.
The "Persian Gulf" sheet is a magnificent rendering
of the Near East; the Gulf of Aden sheet covers Abyssinia and the original "Saba" from which the Queen
of Sheba took her title. A selection of four—China,
Mongolia, Japan and Manchuria—cut to taste, and
mounted and folded, cover the Far East. South Russia,
Siberia and Kamchatka are all available, and the
"Malay Peninsula" takes most of Burma, Siam and
Indo-China as well. The Bridge from Singapore to
Port Darwin is given on two separate sheets of "the
East Indies", also at 1/4M.

Africa is the continent which seems to call one
back most insistently. The best general map of all
that part which flies the Union Jack, or which lies
close around, is the War Office 1/2M. Starting from
Cape Town, four sheets—the Cape of Good Hope,
Natal, S.-W. Africa and the Transvaal—cut and
mounted to taste, take in everything up to Buluwayo.
If the itinerary is via Lobito Bay and Elizabethville,
the Benguella and Upper Congo sheets lead right into
the heart of Africa. The Rhodesias, Nyassaland and
the routes to Beira, are covered by the Upper Congo,
Rhodesia, Zanzibar and Mozambique sheets, and
again a judicious cutting and mounting will make an
ideal general map. For the East Coast, the sheets may
have to be cut and patched, but the Kenya sheet by
itself stretches from Mombasa to Entebbe. The Guinea,
Gold Coast and Nigeria sheets take in all the West
Coast Colonies save the Gambia—that river entirely
surrounded by politics—which comes on the Senegal

sheet. Egypt and the Anglo-Egyptian Sudan are available too at this scale, but perhaps the most convenient map of the Sudan is at 1/3M (also War Office). For the rest of Northern Africa, in particular the French parts thereof, sheets 1 and 2 of the 1/5M published by the " Service Géographique de l'Armée " are excellent general maps. If a general key to the whole of Africa is required, get the 1/16M political map of Africa published by the War Office.

North America offers a considerable choice. The most convenient and easiest to procure is Bartholomew's 1/5M of the United States and part of Canada. The Canadian Department of the Interior has a physical map of Canada at the scale of 60 miles to the inch (1/3,801,600) which is rather large for convenience with its 38 × 58 inches. There is another at 100 miles to the inch (1/6,336,000) which is more convenient, perhaps, but does not offer very much information. The United States Geological Survey issues a map of the U.S.A. in three sheets at 1/2½M, which is rather more fitted for the table than the armchair. Messrs. George Phillips publish a map of the United States in seven sheets at the scale of 1/2½M.

Bartholomew's map of South America (1/10M) is the most convenient for that vast country, and Phillips' commercial map of South America 1/5M is an alternative.

Australia is another case where the Bartholomew (1/6M) is the best available general map. There is a series of four sheets published by Messrs. Robinson of Sydney at the scale of 50 miles to the inch (1/3,168,000) giving little more information, and there is a single sheet map produced by the Property and Survey Department, Canberra, at the scale of 1/5,400,000.

New Zealand is also best shown, generally, by Bartholomew at the scale of 1/2M.

In this matter of the general map the members of the National Geographical Society of the United States are lucky, for they, and apparently only they, can get copies of an excellent series produced by that body. These include one of Canada, the U.S.A. and Mexico at 1/5,193,520, and others of South America, Asia, Europe and the Near East, and Africa, ranging from 1/15M to 1/5M.

The international 1/M map offers considerably more information than any of the above, but for a longish tour is almost too big and requires too many sheets. The index of the sheets covering Europe is given in Chapter XIII, and fuller indexes covering the world can be seen at Stanford's, or procured from the Ordnance Survey, Southampton.

Holidays spent abroad at some definite place will be the pleasanter for maps at larger scales. To consider these in detail would require not a chapter but a volume. In Europe the question presents few difficulties because of the multitude of booksellers and stationers who are ready to supply and to advise. It is, however, a wise precaution to see, as one always can at Messrs. Stanfords Ltd. of 12/14 Long Acre and of 43 Whitehall, what is available. Many of us have found more difficulty in France than elsewhere in Europe. It is curious how easy it is, there, to buy a motor map and how difficult to procure a topographical. The easiest way is to go, or write, to the " Service Géographique de l'Armée, 140 Rue de Grenelles, Paris, 7e " (quite close to the Hôtel des Invalides).

Perhaps the best maps for a holiday which will include a certain amount of excursion, are those published at scales of 1/200,000, 1/300,000, or 1/250,000 (practically our ¼-inch). The range of decimal scales between the normal 1/50,000 or 1/100,000 and the 1/M varies a good deal in the different countries, since the decimal principle, and that of halving from the greater to the less (as in our 1-inch, ½-inch, and ¼-inch), do not combine well. There will always be one of the three, however, and the great benefit of procuring them in advance is that they are not generally available locally except in the " paper flat " form. They can be mounted and folded easily enough in England.

It is to Messrs. Stanfords that one goes for the excellent maps produced by the Survey of India and for those issued by the Survey Departments of the Crown Colonies. There are quantities of useful maps at all sorts of scales issued by the War Office. The latest catalogue of these maps, published by the Geographical Section of the General Staff, is dated 1935 and costs 1s. 6d. In the Crown Colonies the most helpful person will be the man (Director-General, or Surveyor-General) who is responsible for official mapping. He usually has a local 1/M completely up to date, and a variety of other scales.

Car travel is an entirely different question. To start with, the number of roads available is nowhere so large as in England, and the country is almost always less developed. There are far fewer alternatives and a greater need for expert advice. Official topographical maps are not nearly so helpful as in England whereas signposts are generally more so. As journeys are like to be much longer than in England, questions of surface and repair are more important. Everywhere, then, motor associations or firms supply the want and issue up-to-date guides to road surface and classification. One of the most useful services which our motoring associations offer to their members is the supply of all such motoring information. Here are the names of one or two of the many maps which are at the service of members of the Automobile Association.

" Michelin "—Guides, which cover France, Spain, Portugal, Belgium, Luxembourg, and parts of Holland and Italy (from 1/M to 1/100,000).

Michelin—*Routes Rapides* (a yearly revision).

Österreich Touring Clubs—Strasen Karte (Austria).

Deutsche Automobil Club—Strassen Zustande (Germany).

Magyar Touring Club (Hungary).

Service Map of France and Belgium (Automobile Association).

It is wisest to ask which is the best and most up to date in each case. The A.A. will know.

With one or other of the general maps mentioned above, and full motoring information from the A.A., a journey by car will offer no difficulties of route or position.

CHAPTER XVIII

The Field Work of Mapping

[The greater part of this chapter is taken direct from the " Listener ".]

THERE can be few professions which offer a pleasanter mixture of indoor and outdoor craftsmanship than does that of a map-maker, which perhaps partly accounts for its age. In the making of large-scale plans there has been little change for two or three thousand years. Egyptian pictures show chainmen complete with their chains, rodmen with their offset rods, and tape-boys, just exactly as they are to-day.

Triangles.

It is not for nothing that on every map or plan you will see amongst the conventional signs small triangles with little central dots. These are points of the triangulation, and we must begin with them, for a triangle is the start and the framework of all surveying. Supposing that you take three lengths of wood and bolt their ends together you will find that no pressure will alter the shape of the triangle they form. On the other hand, take four lengths of wood and bolt them together to form any four-sided figure and the smallest pressure will make it collapse; for the triangle is rigid and the four-sided figure is not, unless one or another diagonal is added to convert the quadrilateral into two triangles It is for that very simple reason that all land measurements since surveying began are made in triangles. Triangles probably suggest to most people the use of the theodolite and what we call to-day " triangulation ", but indeed the chain surveyor of the past, before theodolites were invented, worked equally in triangles. The difference between then and now lies in the fact that *he* was obliged to measure each side of his triangle, whereas to-day, working with a theodolite, *we* measure only one side (or base) and the two angles which the other two sides make with that base.

Chaining.

The British surveyor of the eighteenth century, whose instruments are so well shown at the Ashmolean in Oxford, measured all his sides, and measured them with a Gunter's chain, which is divided into 100 links —the 100 links equalling 66 feet. Quite contrary to general opinion, we have always been champions of decimal measurement and the Gunter's chain of 66 feet is for use in a decimalized acre, since an acre is our normal measure of area. Let us discuss, then, how he did his survey, and let us take as an illustration a property consisting of a four-sided field within which lay a house, its garden, and its outbuildings. The surveyor would first measure the four sides of the figure, as the most important, or main, lines of his survey, including amongst them one or another of the diagonals, in order to turn the four-sided figure into two rigid triangles. He would start the measurement of any one side as follows. His first station would be near, but just inside one of the corners of the property. From that point a straight line would be laid out, and marked, leading to a similar point just at the corner and just inside the property at the other end of one of the sides. The distance would then be measured in successive lengths of the chain, drawn straight along the line. The chain itself, divided into 100 links, is marked with brass tabs of different shapes so as to save the labour of counting individual links all the way along. The line itself, however, has no particular value. Its object is to facilitate the survey of the paths, fences, and detail of the property. These matters must be tabulated in the surveyor's field book. On a page of that book the chain line is represented by two parallel lines, up the centre, just so far apart that distances in links can be booked inside. Suppose that the first chain length crosses a path, the edge of which measured $7\frac{1}{2}$ links from his starting station. Then in the book opposite the number $7\frac{1}{2}$, there would be drawn diagrammatically the edge of that path. The other edge of the path would probably occur at some such point as 10 or 11 links and would also be booked. This exceedingly simple measurement and booking would be applied to every point of detail along the line. But the hedge itself would not, we will suppose, cross the measured line at all. It would lie within some 10 to 20 links to one side of it. In order to complete the survey, distances from the chain line to the fence must be "offset", that is to say, that every so often—say, at every twentieth link (in any case at every corner or change of direction)—a surveyor's rod would be laid out at right-angles to the chain line, and the actual distance to the hedge would be recorded in the book.

Now we will suppose that all the sides of the property including one diagonal have been so surveyed and recorded, and that there still remain certain things to survey too far off existing lines to offset. In that case other chained lines would be measured, connecting marked points on the main lines. The exact points of start and finish and all the survey measurements would be noted of course in the surveyor's book. Finally, the whole survey would be plotted on paper at some convenient scale (say forty feet to the inch). Now I am going to make one further supposition—supposing that the house inside this property lies right in the middle so as to make the measurement of a diagonal impossible.

Then the survey would be divided not into two triangles but into three, so that the house should be avoided, and yet all information concerning it should be properly booked.

The Theodolite.

A certain Dutchman called Snellius made the first triangulation with an instrument designed to measure angles. The date of this notable advance is 1615, and it is one which wholly transformed the ordinary process of surveying. It became, you see, possible to confine tape measurement to one length (or base) only, and then, by measuring the angles of the first triangle, to calculate mathematically, rather than to measure, the two remaining sides of that triangle. Having computed those two sides, two more triangles can be extended from them, and so on *ad infinitum*.

Baselines.

The invariable beginning, however, is the measurement of one side, and it may be done in innumerable different ways. One of the early ways was to tie a bit of string, or make some other visible mark, on a wheel. Then the number of times that wheel revolves in its journey along the line multiplied by the circumference, naturally gives the distance. In property surveying, however, before angular measurement with the theodolite, the chain was normally employed. A century and a half ago various other substitutes began to make their appearance. The earliest of our English bases was that measured by General Roy on Hounslow Heath. Both wooden and glass rods were employed.

A development which underlies the whole fabric of the Ordnance Survey of Great Britain was the compensating bars invented by General Colby. Metals have their own peculiar co-efficients of expansion. They grow longer when heated, shorter when cooled. But if we are to measure a distance accurately on the ground, it is obvious that we must know accurately the length of the measuring rod or chain. General Colby had the rather brilliant thought that if he made a composite bar of two different metals, connecting them, but not rigidly, and had, at each end, little cross-bars capable of movement, the ends of these little cross-bars might be made to express an invariable length. Colby's compensating bars were used for the two bases, at Salisbury Plain and Loch Foyle, which are the starting points of the British triangulation. Nowadays bases are measured with tapes or wires of invar—a certain metallic alloy which is not without its drawbacks but which is little affected by change of temperature.

General Roy.

The first instance of a large survey in Great Britain was Roy's map of the Highlands. This was made just after the '45 Rebellion. Now Roy's map rests upon a triangulation, but not one done with a theodolite. It was in fact observed with the compass. On this compass skeleton—a skeleton which showed the relatively true positions of the important summits of Scotland—was built up the map, partly by chain measurement, in the old way, and partly by compass traverse. No doubt it was because the compass entered so largely into the construction of this map that what we should now call the " fair drawing " was then described as the " fair protraction ". The angles were plotted with a protractor.

The Ordnance Survey.

Roy's " promised land ", which he did not live to see, was a proper consistent and general survey of Great Britain, the Ordnance Survey of to-day. To describe its making we must start with the triangulation, which provides the fixed points in Great Britain upon which the map is built up. There are more than 150,000 of them. The measured lengths and bases of Great Britain are, as we have seen, those at Salisbury Plain and at Loch Foyle. These two are connected by a triangulation (or series of triangles) of which the angles were measured with a very large theodolite made by Ramsden, who flourished in the seventeen-eighties.

The Great Triangulation.

Ramsden's great theodolite has been used on all important features of Great Britain. There is practically no large hill in Great Britain which it and its brother instrument have not seen. It was a surveyor using it in Cumberland to whom Wordsworth addressed a famous poem, and with reference to its use on the top of St. Paul's there occurred an interesting controversy with a very eminent society. That society pointed out how unedifying it was that a rude and brutal soldiery should be perched upon the top of a sacred edifice and that soldiers were by nature, education, and training obviously unequal to the task of computing from their observations with due and proper scientific accuracy. Fortunately no very great attention appears to have been paid to the protest. And so Ordnance surveyors extended over Great Britain a triangulation which, although one hundred years old, still serves its purpose.

It covers the land with accurately fixed points distant from each other about ten miles. Distances of ten miles are, however, too large to govern a subsequent chain survey. The large triangles had to be cut up into smaller ones by inserting more stations, and here we begin the description of the actual process of the detail survey. Just ahead of the actual chain surveyors came a trigonometrical observer who filled in the gaps in the major triangulations and provided fixed points at distances from each other of about $1\frac{1}{2}$ miles. He was accompanied by two or three labourers, who erected his signals and marked the points over which his theodolite had been erected. As the triangulator observed his angles he recorded them in a book, which was forwarded to the Central Office, and there a computer solved his triangles in order to find out whether all his work had been good. If it had been all was well, but, if not, the triangulator had to go back and re-observe certain angles. The computer's work was to calculate the length of all the sides of all the triangles.

The Detail Survey.

These sides were used as the main lines of the chain surveyor who followed the trigonometrical observer on the ground. The chain surveyor would, of course, always find it necessary to amplify the main triangulated lines with other minor or " split " lines. The chain surveyor's book was then sent to the office and the first thing to do was to compare the chained lengths with those calculated from the triangulation. If they agreed within one point in a thousand or so the chain surveyor was considered to have done his work well, but if not he had to rechain.

The records were next given to a man called the line plotter. The line plotter plotted out these various triangles on paper to see whether everything closed correctly. If it did not, the work was again sent back to the field; but if it did, matters passed to the detail plotter. Now the detail plotter's task was not only to plot the lines afresh, but to plot from the offsets those houses, roads, paths, railways and other details which completed the survey. When the detail plot was finished it was traced, and the tracing was set out on the ground again in the hands of a man known as the examiner. The examiner has to see that the finally plotted map really corresponds with nature. The way in which he does so is interesting and simple. Supposing that you walk along a road until looking, shall we say, to the right, you see three points on that side of the road all in one straight line cutting the path where you stand. Those three points might be the corner of the nearest house, the corner of a fence standing behind, and a distant

chimney. If these three points form a straight line
in nature so should they also on the plan. It is not
always easy to find three such points, but two will
serve. Supposing that the edge of the nearest house
and the corner of the field behind are in a line which
cuts the fence where you stand at a point twenty-seven
links from the nearest hedge junction. Measure it both
on the ground and on the map and see whether you
get, as you should do, the same answer. If not, then a
mistake has been made. The examiner also inserted all
the boundaries (consulting the local authorities in doing
so), investigated the names, and finished off the plan.

But his work was no more to be trusted than that
of anybody else, and it was therefore passed to a final
examiner who went over the ground again, or a considerable portion of it, to see where he could find a
flaw. Supposing he found none, the work would be
forwarded to the officer in charge of that particular
division, who would put the last and final check upon
selected plans.

The Levelling.

The field work is now complete, except for the
levelling and benchmarks. The triangulation, you will
remember, covered the ground so that fixed points are
as close to each other as $1\frac{1}{2}$ miles. The levelling is
of the same density. There must be a primary level
net of long and very precisely measured lines; there
must be dependent on those main lines many others
of a lesser significance joining point to point; and then
contemporary with the actual detail survey comes a
tertiary levelling which supplies benchmarks within $1\frac{1}{4}$
miles of each other. These benchmarks are, you know,
on the bridges, on steps of churches, on porches, on
any other permanent detail, and show the height above
mean sea level. The leveller, having taken his observations, records them in a book just as did the surveyor,
and sends them into the office. Heights are then com-

puted. If they check out well they are accepted; if not the levels must be taken again. When they are finally established they are passed over to a plotter who plots upon the final plan the position of each benchmark and adds its height. Then the whole plan goes into the hands of the man who measures up areas, and of many competent and indispensable examiners, until eventually it is ready for reproduction.

That is the way in which a 25-inch plan is made. Now a 6-inch plan is made directly from it by reduction in the camera. It has to be redrawn because you cannot reduce a plan to a sixteenth of its size and retain legibility of the names and conventional signs.

Newer Methods.

We have talked so far about old but good methods of survey, used everywhere still to-day. There are new methods, and the impulse is always to consider that the newer must needs be the better. That, of course, is far from being the case, but it is true that every method has its place. Let us consider some of them. One important group measures distances optically instead of with chain and tape. The most flexible and perfect little instrument of this sort is human eyesight. A small base (the distance between the eyes) and an instinctive measurement of angles from it gives us our normal idea of distance. This same system is used in range finders, telemeters, and other instruments with formidable names. If we were to do an original survey in England to-day it is quite possible that we should adopt one or other of these optical methods of measuring distance. Then there are various photographic methods of survey. In mountainous countries, like the Rockies or the Alps, surveys can be made by using a camera instead of a theodolite or plane table, and by making the necessary measurements upon the resulting photographic plate. Such methods cannot do away with the need for an initial triangulation, because the true position of the camera, during exposure, must be known.

Surveying from the Air.

Much more familiar to the public, however, and much more interesting in its way, is survey from air photographs. An air photograph is generally so taken as to look as nearly as possible vertically downwards upon the ground below. Supposing that the aeroplane flies straight and level, and not too fast, and supposing that the ground underneath is as level and as clearly marked out as that chessboard upon which Alice played in Looking-glass Land, the subsequent survey would indeed be a simple and obvious task. Unfortunately these desirable conditions are never found in conjunction. An air photograph is a flat piece of paper, whilst the ground is very seldom flat. Even with dimensions, threes into twos won't go. Supposing that you are looking down upon the top of Ben Nevis, the summit will look as much too large comparatively as the boots of some unwary prone victim of the snapshot fiend in front. We can and do overcome all such difficulties, but only by surveying on the image instead of on the original. Sometimes the image is the best to use; sometimes the original. In neither case can you survey unless you can see, and the camera can only record what it does see from the air.

The methods of survey which I have outlined are those normal for a really large scale; for plans rather than for maps. But, once done, every sort of map can be based upon it. In this country we have but the one survey. It is suitable for 25 inches to the mile, but by successive reductions it is equally available for a scale of 25 miles to the inch.

Plane Tabling.

The problem is quite a different one where the first map—say a $\frac{1}{2}$-inch or $\frac{1}{4}$-inch—is to be made of some

colony.   Come with me to the Orange Free State in
the Dominion of South Africa and I will tell you something of such a survey.

Please think of a small party consisting of two officers
and five N.C.O.'s.   The first thing, just as in the survey
of England, was to extend a triangulation all over the
country.

The officers moved some ten to twenty miles every
day.   Transport consisted of wagons, Scotch carts and
Cape carts, all mule-drawn.   The normal evening camp
was underneath some hill upon which a trigonometrical
station was that evening erected and observed from.
Every two or three weeks the two officers would meet
and compare notes, calculate the results of their observations and be ready to plot fresh boards for the plane
tablers who followed after them.   Now let us visit
one of the N.C.O.'S and see how the plane table works.
A plane table is nothing else than a small board mounted
upon a tripod.   The board or plane table top (plane
because it is levelled in a horizontal plane) is covered
with linen-backed white paper and on that white
paper are plotted, in their proper relative positions,
the fixed points provided by the officers.   Opposite
each little plotted triangle is given its appropriate
height above mean sea level.   The plane tabler's task
is to complete the map, filling in the whole of the detail
of nature upon that skeleton and to add the appropriate
names and data.   This he does by sighting along a
ruler with sights at each end of it.   The theory of plane
tabling is simple in the extreme, but the practice demands experience, skill, neat fingers, absolute honesty,
and robust health.   The work has then to be so neatly
penned in that a draughtsman, thousands of miles
away, may fair draw without mistake or misunder-
standing.

That sort of plane table survey is extremely good for
scales of about 1 inch, $\frac{1}{2}$-inch, or $\frac{1}{4}$-inch to the mile.
It is not, of course, suitable for such large and important

work as our 25-inch of England. But I can wish no man a more attractive life, and it is one which will demand in the future the services of an increasing number of Englishmen until the British Empire is mapped according to its possibilities.

Revision.

A house once finished starts on a life of repairs; a road programme is no sooner complete than surfaces demand attention, and no map can continue to serve its purpose without periodical revision. That revision should take place at intervals dictated by the amount of change. In Great Britain the statutory periods before the Great War were twenty years for the plans and fifteen for the maps. These intervals have lengthened seriously since then, but we must hope for better times. In the paragraph on the detail survey the examiner was mentioned. When the original survey was finished the examiner automatically became the reviser using exactly the same semigraphic methods. In Chapter XVI the addition to a plan of a new house is illustrated. Anything new can be added to a really accurate survey with little trouble, because there is so much already mapped to which to refer. Naturally additions are difficult to make on an old plan which has lain in store for years and which perhaps has expanded or contracted by very plottable amounts. Revisers are equipped with fresh prints on special tracing paper, and work with little else than linen tape and sketching case. If much change has taken place some new lines must be measured with the chain, and sometimes air photographs are a help. In the course of revision new names have to be recorded in the name books and new boundaries mered and plotted. When the reviser has finished, a "final reviser" goes over it again, checking here and there, altering, if he must, in a different colour, and accepting the fuller responsibility.

PLATE VIII

A PLANE TABLER ON THE GREAT LAKES

Revision of the 1-inch differs a good deal from the revision of the plans. The 1-inch reviser is given the latest edition of the 6-inch, and it is at this scale that he inserts everything new. As the 1-inch must be generalized, and roads particularly must be shown at much more than their actual widths, revision is a study of what must be left out, as well as of what must be added. Once the 6-inch is revised it is sent to the office and there fair drawn on the scale of two inches to the mile. It is only in the final stages that it is photographically reduced to the 1-inch.

AUTHORITIES TO CONSULT ON SURVEYING

General.

Text Book of Topographical Surveying. 3rd Edition, 1925 (H.M.S.O.). 15s.

Mathematical.

Survey Computations, 8s. *Field Astronomy*, 12s. 6d. (H.M.S.O., 1932.)

Special.

Surveying from Air Photographs. Hotine, 1931 (Constable).

Organized Plane Tabling (Ordnance Survey, 1931). 2s. 6d.

Topography in the Tropical Forest Belt (Ordnance Survey, 1931). 2s. 6d.

CHAPTER XIX

The Office Work of Mapping

Drawing.

AFTER check and countercheck the records of the field work come to the office, the field surveyor starts afresh on his new area, and the office sorts out his finished material and begins to get busy. The first step is to get "blues" of the new survey, or prints, in blue, obtained by the joint efforts of those photographers and provers we shall meet, more familiarly, later on. It is on a blue that the draughtsman finally draws, and the "blue" is because the camera, when it comes to rephotography, is blind to that colour and records only the black which is drawn over it. The draughtsman, equipped with a battery of pens and compasses, draws his outline (which is finally to appear in black) with an eye on where the names will come. He may have to break a road or a fence to get one in. His roads are gauged to size, he has models for the strength of this or that line, and he follows precedent in the shape and size of his conventions. If it is a plan he is drawing (and is to be all in black) every item is drawn on one sheet of paper, and finished with the exception of the names, the parcel and other numbers, the area figures (in acres and decimals thereof) and the benchmarks and heights. This nearly completed sheet is then examined and goes on to the typer and stamper for the addition of names and numbers. This man has next him a selection of lead type. His first step is to classify a name as coming within such and such a sort of alphabet. The letters are put into a palette, dabbed over with the correct ink and down goes the name into place. The acreages have already been pencilled in the correct positions on the plan, and the typer and stamper deals with them too. Then levels and benchmarks have to be stamped on; and at every stage the magisterial eye of an examiner picks out shaky line or defective shape, lack of depth in the black, or, what is worse, the occasional error. In examining any map one has to divide it into small bits and concentrate on each in turn. The usual way is to cut a rectangle in a piece of tracing paper, to place the latter over the plan, and to deal with that area, and mark it off, before going on to the next.

Draughtsmen who are doing small scale, or coloured, map-work, have other duties which will be described presently, but meanwhile we must follow the plan, which we have just drawn, on to the zinc printing plate. The plan has been drawn at the size at which it is to be printed. It can go direct to zinc therefore without bothering the camera to reduce its size. The zinc plate is carefully grained and then coated with a solution sensitive to light. It is then put in a large glass frame with the drawn plan face down upon it. The two are clamped together and the air is pumped out of the frame to ensure a really intimate touch between paper and zinc. Then the frame is put out in sunlight, or exposed to an arc-lamp, the zinc plate is developed and the plan has passed from the paper to the plate. This process is called vandyking.

Next we must get back to the draughtsman and consider a coloured map. In this case the great difficulty is to get a perfect map "register". That is, each colour must fall into its right place. A blue stream must pass under a black bridge, and a brown contour must bend exactly on that blue stream. All the printing plates must therefore be of exactly the same size. The usual practice is to have three "key" plates separately drawn for black detail, blue water, and brown contours respectively, and to provide the other colours from " off-sets ", which we shall get to presently. Instead of one blue to draw on we now want three, and these printed on first-class paper one after the other. Each is then drawn upon in black, but each records only its own subject. The model, of course, has everything upon it, and all of it appears on each of the blue prints; but the water plate (to consider only one of the three key plates) drawn in black over the streams, lakes and coast, and then re-photographed, loses the blue outline of contours and detail and is automatically sorted out.

On the best class of map the draughtsman writes the names as he goes. Nothing good happens without care, however. Every name is gauged, and maybe slightly larger or smaller, slightly squeezed up or opened out, as the situation demands. The correct alphabet must be used, and it should be impossible, on any map, to say Jones wrote these names or Smith made those cuttings and embankments. In order that every little weakness may disappear, and every line be firm and sharp, this class of drawing is done at a scale larger than the printed map is to show. The drawing is then reduced, photographically, to the final scale. The 1-inch is drawn at two inches to the mile; the $\frac{1}{4}$-inch on a $\frac{1}{2}$-inch model, and so on. Now comes the draughtsman's last job which takes him to the camera-room. Here, on the easel, he pins up his detail plate, places his water plate exactly on top, " needling it " into position, adds the contour plate on top again, and returns to his room to start the next sheet. Quite a fascinating bit of craftsmanship is map-drawing.

Photography.

The camera man of a big mapping office will have lenses big enough to cover the wall of a big room, and a body to his camera large enough to hold a com-

PLATE IX

(*above*) DRAWING THE MAP
(*below*) TIMING AN EXPOSURE

mittee meeting in. He can get a reverse or direct image
because he can photograph direct or through an invert-
ing prism. The glass negative is, of course, very large,
for it has to cover the size of the largest map. The
largest in use at the Ordnance Survey is 48 × 33 inches,
and weighs about 40 lb. The film is of collodion, sensitized with silver nitrate, and the negative is exposed
wet. Both arc-lamps and mercury-vapour tubes are
used during exposure. Photographically the aim is
to secure the most perfect definition from the original,
and cartographically to secure that exact shape and
scale essential if one colour is to fit upon another. For
normal map work the camera has to fit the three key
plates, black, blue and brown, exactly. It has been
explained how these are pinned up one over the other
(each consisting of several independently drawn portions). The photographer, keeping to the same setting
and focus, photographs each one in turn, unpinning
and removing as he does so. Generally speaking he
has to reduce the size of the original to half on the
plate.

One of the disadvantages of the old copperplate
alphabets was that the very fine lines and " serifs "
(or ticks on the tops and bottoms of letter strokes)
often failed to appear whole and undamaged on the
developed plate. But there may be other similar breaks
or blemishes due to insufficiently dense black ink, and
it may be necessary to prolong exposure and so to
lose contrast. The negative wants a lot of touching
up and so it goes on next to the " photo-writer ". He
may have to strengthen the background with photo-
pake, or to cut (with a fine steel point) such lines as
have not photographed well, but are broken. There
may be bubble marks, perhaps, or slight breaks between
different portions of the same map. There is opportunity here also for making additions or corrections and
for adding fresh marginal notes. When special (or
district) maps are made up from portions of the normal

sheets the photographic department does most of the work.

But one does not print from glass and therefore the next stage is to pass the work from glass to zinc. We have seen above how work from paper may go direct to the zinc by a process known as vandyking. To do the same with a negative and a sensitized sheet of zinc is known as heliozincography. In the first process the dark lines on paper are preserved on the plate, in the latter the clear or transparent lines of the negative. The same frames are used as in vandyking.

Proving and Litho-drawing.

Whether the process has been " vandyke " or " helio " the plates now go to the prover, and we get to the " zincography " part of the process. When lithography, and then zincography, first challenged copper engraving and printing, the map was drawn in greasy ink direct upon the stone, or else upon transfer paper which was laid down upon the prepared stone or zinc surface and passed, or transferred, the map to it. Many minor corrections, scales, marginal notes, and so forth, are still added to the printing record in this way. The next stage in the development of map preparation came with the invention of photozincography; the transfer by photo-mechanical means of the original to a zinc printing plate, of which mention has already been made. This invention, simultaneous in England and Australia, should no doubt have been the crown and coping stone of a patient investigation directed to that end alone. It will surprise few, however, to find that the real genesis was much more human. " I was staying in the Isle of Wight," writes General Sir Henry James, " and whilst there a lady asked me if I knew of any means by which she could get some etchings . . . copied and printed in an inexpensive manner . . . the next day I had a chromo-carbon print taken and transferred to zinc and this was the

first photozincograph ever taken here or elsewhere "
(1859). The discovery was to have an immediate consequence. On the very next day Sir Henry James was
at the Treasury in London to discuss his estimates for
the forthcoming year. The Chancellor of the moment
was no less a person than Mr. Gladstone. Now Mr.
Gladstone was anxious to get copied some of the rarer
treasures of the Record Office. Sir Henry James, the
infallible, immediately undertook the work, and for
some ten years the Ordnance Survey copied and dis-
tributed such national treasures as William the Con-
queror's Domesday Book, Magna Charta, and the
Down Survey of Ireland.

The litho draughtsman and prover have lost a part of
their original programme, therefore, but have acquired
a very large new field of activity in preparing the many
colour plates which are now required. The key plates
for a map such as the 1-inch are the black (detail),
blue (water) and brown (contour). A job such as filling
in the road colours is done as follows:

The detail plate would be taken, and from it made a
" pull " or print in ordinary printer's ink. On the
greasy lines of this pull an aniline dye is sprinkled.
The paper is then freed of any superfluous dye, which
adheres to the greasy impression and can be blown off
the white portions. The pull is then laid down on a
fresh stone or zinc plate and the dye sinks in, leaving
an exact key to the road margins. Using these margins,
and " gumming out " every part of the plate save the
roads, the plate is then made ready for the appropriate
colour. Layers are prepared on a key of the contour
plate and so on.

It is normal in ordinary map work to use a plate for
each colour, although that colour may be in various
different tones or shades. In such difficult colour
printing as is characteristic of geological maps, the
various colours are produced from a few " primary "
plates. In this as in most colour work different shades

are produced by printing in parallel lines or rulings. If the lines are very close together (say 85 to the inch) the shade is dark, if the liners are opener (say 40 to the inch) the shade is lighter. If the ruling is crossed (at right angles) by another ruling the shade becomes darker again. The present arrangement for printing geological maps depends upon the "Improved Scheme B" worked out by two enthusiasts, Messrs. Young and Pettet, in 1911. The primary colours, blue, red and yellow, are taken in two different tints of each, one light and one dark. Each of these six tints is given a simple ruling, a cross ruling, and a "solid" (or continuous colour). The result is eighteen varieties of colour. Wherever rulings are in question in combining varieties the lines of each particular tint are given their own angle, so that the lines of various colours never overprint when used in conjunction with each other, and blend rather than quarrel.

The next stage is to combine any two of these eighteen by overprinting one upon the other. The number of shades available rises to 153. Now using three printings the number available rises to 693 and by arranging for a certain number of "four printings" a total of 750 provides for every likely contingency. The model of those various shades has, under each variety, a record of the primary plates used in its production.

The litho draughtsman must often work backwards (as in a looking-glass) because many printing machines reverse the image in passing it from stone, or zinc, to paper. It is, in fact, only those "off-set" machines which print from the plate on to a rubber cylinder, and from the rubber to paper, which give a direct image. Of the two craftsmen here considered the litho draughtsman may be said to be the artist, and the prover the mechanic; although there is no very hard-and-fast line to draw, and both are men of taste as well as of skill.

With his etches and gums the prover prepares each

plate so that, in the machine, the ink will hold on prepared greasy surface and will make no mark on those parts left clean and wet.   The final proof, a complete colour model, is sent for inspection; and that generally means remarks.   There is a spot on the blue plate; such and such a contour is just out of place on a stream, a name is too heavy or a road improperly classified.   These the litho draughtsman and prover attend to, until, inspection satisfied, the plates go on to the machine.

Co-operation.

It may be of interest to take a definite job and see how the various trades, so far mentioned, dovetail into each other.   The example shall be the preparation of a Geological 1-inch on the " New Series " (see Chapter XIV).   The topography of this series (the second edition) is still upon the copper plate, which served for its printing up to 1880.   But printing from copper is fastish at twenty or so an hour.   The first step is therefore for the prover to take a transfer from the copper and lay it on stone, from which 800 an hour may be printed.   From this printing stone he pulls a copy in blue.   This is forwarded to the Geological Survey and on it is drawn (in black) a model of the revised geological information.   When the new model comes back from the Geological Survey a draughtsman adds to it (also in black) certain " key " points, road junctions and the like, which will help to set the geology exactly into position on the outline.   The photographer next photographs this drawing, enlarging it to $1\frac{1}{2}$ inches to the mile, develops a zinc plate with the work on it (heliozincography), and the prover pulls a proof in blue and passes it to the draughtsman.   The draughtsman " fair draws " the geological overprint, passes it back to the photographer, who photographs down from the $1\frac{1}{2}$-inch to the 1-inch scale, passes the result to a zinc plate as before, and sends the latter back to the prover. The prover takes a transfer from this zinc plate and lays it on the original stone (the copy of the copper plate). In doing so he fits it very carefully on the witness points which the draughtsman added to key outline and geology together. The detail and geological outline can now be printed together in black from the completed stone. The geology has to be given its characteristic colourings, however. Six printings go to the complete colour scheme, but three only will be required and three models on stone on which the colours may be prepared. The prover prepares these other stones by " off-sets " from his original, and on to each of them transfers, from copper, the rulings (or systems of parallel straight lines) in which that particular colour is to be printed. Finally he passes all the stones to the machine printer who completes the job.

Machine Printing.

Meanwhile the machine minder has cleaned up; washed the ink of the last run from his rollers, oiled his machine and prepared for the next run. The machine feeder is ready with a store of seasoned paper. The new plate is put in, and the run starts. If the run, or edition, is to be a short one the machine to use is a flat-bed, printing about 800 an hour. It is an easy type to start things on, and to get register between successive plates. If the run is long then a rotary offset, printing up to 2000 an hour, will be better, even if the machine minder takes longer to arrange and to get register. It is a rotary offset printing machine which is shown in the frontispiece (Plate I). For several similar colour maps three or four rotaries will be used as a " battery " so that colours may follow each other quickly. Before the word go is given there is, probably, an examination of a machine proof. When the run is over and the edition complete, the plates go back to the prover to be gummed up and put away, safe from dust and damp, in the rack. In the Ordnance Survey there are over 200,000 of these zinc plates ready to hand for reprints.

Mounting and Folding.

From the printing shop printed maps go off to the mounting-room. Most maps are linen backed since few buy the " paper flat " or " paper folded ". The mounting machine is a mass of rollers and drums. Linen and maps go in at one end, the maps are pasted on the linen, the gas-heated drums dry them off and roll them to a proper fit, and the machine delivers, at the other end, a long band of linen with maps on it, cutting each one off as a final operation. The guillotine man then trims all the sheets to size and sends them off for folding and covering. It is curious that no machinery has yet been devised for folding the map in two directions. The folding machine will do (say) three folds from north to south, or six perhaps from east to west, but an attempt to do one after the other results in bursts. The air imprisoned within the folds has, so far, baffled machinery. The last fold is made by hand therefore; and then the cover is well and truly pasted into place. In this office the girls do the section mounting, for such as prefer that style.

The last trip of the completed map is to store, there to take a place on the shelf until the agents secure it.

Administration.

A map or plan in its journey through the various stages of preparation misses out certain offices which have, for all that, had much to do with its make up. For example, one office has been constantly at work upon providing, and repairing, that control of fixed points and heights to which it must conform. Another dictates the measures to be dealt with by the surveyors or revisers in the field, supplies them with material, explains new legislation affecting their work, watches progress and criticizes their results. Another orders paper almost by the train load, supplies all material, and fines the unfortunate whose wife has appropriated the office knife. One of the most interesting safely stores all the records of a hundred and fifty years. Here you may see the field books, the plots, the proofs, the publications, and the calculations of the past. A very busy office for its contents are witness to the actual stage of development of any part of the country at the dates of survey or revision. Lastly there is the headquarters which directs and orders, and approves.

And great fun it all is.

INDEX

INDEX

204

Clarke, Colonel A. R., 48.
Classification of roads, 25.
Close, Colonel Sir Charles, 86, 141.
Colby, General, 52, 59, 70, 100, 118, 156, 182.
Cold front, 158.
Colouring conventions, 32.
Colour printing, 74, 75, 197, 198.
Colour washes, 75, 76, 168, 169, 170.
Compass, 87, 116, 117, 118.
Compensating bars (Colby's), 182.
Compulsory area (land registration), 56.
Computer, 185.
Conformal projections, 37, 38.
Conical projections, 40, 41, 42.
Conical orthomorphic projection, 42, 146.
Contours, explanation, 29.
— general on, 29–32, 58, 59, 61, 71, 76, 77, 96, 97, 100, 101.
— interpolated, 76, 77, 101.
— lakebed, 60.
— population, 144.
— pressure, 155.
— submarine (or seabed), 26, 90, 92.
— surveyed, 60, 61, 76, 100.
Contractions, 23, 170.
Conventional signs, map, 24–26, 78, 79.
— plan, 27, 63–66.
— geological, 152.
— meteorological, 162, 163.
Cook, Captain James, 88.
Co-ordinates, 127, 128, 129.
Co-ordinate card, 130.
Copper engraver, 28, 69, 71, 72, 73, 76, 81.
Copperplate, 28, 76, 195.
Copper-printing, 28, 69, 72, 199.
Corps of Royal Military Surveyors and Draughtsmen, 69.
Cost of plans, 66.
— maps, 86.
— charts, 94.
— geological maps, 151.
County of London, plans of, 4, 56.
— registration of property in, 56.
Covers, 20, 74, 131, 137, 201.
Crawford, O. G. S., 145.
Crown Colonies, maps of, 177.
Crowquill nibs, 166.
Cuillins, 13, 137.
Cutter for trimming paper, 170.
Cyclist, maps for, 13.
Cylindrical projections, 37.

Darkest England (epoch map), 58, 144.
Datum, levelling, 59.

Datum, soundings, 90.
Dawson, 100.
Dead ground, 107.
Dead reckoning, 89.
Decimal scales, 21, 22, 23.
Declination, 117.
De la Beche, 148.
Delamere, origin, 44, 71.
Department of Scientific and Industrial Research, 148.
Depression, 156, 157.
Detail plotter, 185.
Detail survey, 184, 185.
Diagrams, traffic or town, 18, 19, 82.
Dip, 116.
Direct image, 195, 198.
Distortions of paper, 23.
District maps, 12, 73, 131, 133.
Draughtsman, 192, 193, 194, 199.
Drawing, 166, 167, 168, 192, 193, 194, 199.
Drawing pen, 166.
Drummond, Captain, 52.
Dunbar tidal station, 59.
Dwerryhouse, A. R., 152.

" *Earth Lore* ", 152.
Echo sounder, 91, 92.
Editions, ordnance small scale, 69–85.
Electrolytic bath, 73.
Engraving, 28, 71, 73, 76, 81.
Epoch maps, 58, 143, 144.
Equal area projections, 38.
— — cylindrical projection, 38.
Equator, 35.
Equidistant cylindrical projection, 37.
Erasures, 168.
Europe, 173, 176.
Examiner, 185, 193.
Examining, 186.
Expansions of paper, 23, 170.
Eye for country, 111, 112.

Faden, W., 69.
Fair drawing, 78, 192, 193, 194, 199.
Fathom, 88, 90, 95.
— lines, 90.
" *Field Astronomy* ", 191.
Field book, 181.
Field work of mapping, Chap. XVIII, 179.
Fifth edition (one inch), 20, 77, 78, 79, 101, 104.
Final reviser, 186, 190.
Five Foot Plan, 4, 53, 54, 56.
Flat wash, 169.
Flour paste, 171.
Folding machine, 201.